HER SECRET
LOVER

by

Judith Arnold

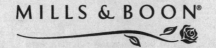

MILLS & BOON®

To Malle Vallik

*MILLS & BOON and MILLS & BOON with the Rose Device
are registered trademarks of the publisher.
TEMPTATION is a registered trademark of
Harlequin Enterprises Limited, used under licence.*

*First published in Great Britain 2000
by Harlequin Mills & Boon Limited,
Eton House, 18-24 Paradise Road, Richmond, Surrey TW9 1SR*

© Barbara Keiler 1999

ISBN 0 263 82384 9

21-0007

*Printed and bound in Spain
by Litografia Rosés S.A., Barcelona*

1

AT SOME POINT in a woman's life, she ought to stop getting sweaty palms in the presence of a sexy guy. Unfortunately, Martha Cooper hadn't reached that point yet.

In her case, at least, twenty-six wasn't old enough. Possession of a master's degree in accounting wasn't educated enough. Owning a small house with a big mortgage and having all the utilities listed under her name wasn't responsible enough. Spending forty-three dollars, not counting the tip, for a haircut wasn't sophisticated enough. Riding five miles to the office on her bicycle that morning wasn't healthy enough.

She sat in the passenger seat of Blake Robey's vintage Mustang convertible, feeling the brisk October night wreak havoc with her forty-three-dollar haircut, and pretended that sitting beside him didn't send every cell in her body into paroxysms of awareness.

It was embarrassing to have a crush on your boss. Even more embarrassing to feel yourself reduced to a jittery collection of anxieties and insecurities when you were sitting only the width of a stick shift away from him, cruising through the starlit Hyannis evening, with the scent of the ocean lacing the air and his profile illuminated by a silver half moon. Most embarrassing of all was knowing that when he thought about you, the first, last and only image that came to his mind was: _accountant_.

"I really appreciate your staying so late," he was saying. The wind swallowed large chunks of his voice, but Martha could still make out what he was saying. It helped too that, like a lovesick schoolgirl, she was hanging on his every word. "I mean, on a Saturday and all."

"The sooner we get settled into the new building, the sooner we can get back to work," she responded. God, she even talked like an accountant.

"Yeah, well, why not?" Blake talked like a barely reformed beach bum. He looked like one, too, with his long, blond hair sun-streaked and his features weathered by the shore winds. He had large shoulders but a lean physique, the kind of sleek build Martha associated with dolphins, or maybe sharks—efficient, aerodynamic and strong.

He wasn't her type. She told herself that every day, several times a day. He was a dashing, daring, devil-may-care entrepreneur who couldn't be bothered with sweating the small stuff. She was a plain, bashful math whiz whose entire professional life revolved around the small stuff and who never made mistakes.

Except for one: getting a crush on Blake Robey. That was a major blunder, no question about it.

She knew all the caveats about becoming involved with one's boss, but none of them applied to her, because she and Blake were never going to become involved. Sharks didn't mate with guppies. Men named Blake, who wore T-shirts to work and owned their own companies because it was more fun than having to work for someone else, and who had rugged shoulders that made a woman's hands ache to be wrapped around them, did not pair up with women who were quiet and well-behaved, and who derived their greatest thrills from running numbers through the computer and having them reconcile correctly. Martha was never going to have an affair with Blake, so office ethics were irrelevant.

Back in July, she'd taken the job with Blake's Fruit Brews on a whim—or more likely, since she wasn't given to whims, she'd taken the job because ten minutes in Blake's presence, discussing the position, had been enough to turn her brain into lime Jell-O. She'd been on vacation then, sharing a beach cottage rental with a few friends for a week. Her second morning at the cottage, while thumbing through the *Cape Cod Times*, she'd noticed an ad announcing an opening for an accountant at Blake's Fruit Brews. She already had an excellent job with a large accounting firm in Boston; she'd landed it straight out of graduate school, and she'd considered herself fortunate to work for a solid, established company. The job paid well, all the perks, all the benefits—but it bored her. It imposed a drab sameness on her existence: dressing up daily in a tailored suit, riding the half-hour commute on the T into the city, analyzing data, filing reports and riding the T home. Although it was exactly what she'd imagined herself doing when she'd finished school, the tedium of it was really getting to her.

And there she'd been, on Cape Cod in July. Something in the summer heat, something in the ubiquitous coconut fragrance of sunblock lotion and the gritty sand burrowed into the carpet of the cottage she and her friends were renting, something in the constant, humid breezes and the charming cafes and boutiques of downtown Hyannis had captivated her. So while her housemates had been sailing around Nantucket Sound on a chartered catamaran for the afternoon, Martha had paid a call on Blake.

Blake Robey had offered her the job on the spot. And whether it had been because she was in a stupor from lolling on the beach the previous day, or because she'd tapped a tiny, hitherto unacknowledged well of adventurousness inside her, or because Blake had the bluest eyes she'd ever seen, she'd accepted.

"You like your new office?" he asked as they stopped at a red light.

"Yes." She should show some enthusiasm. She should tell him she was crazy about her new office, which was twice the size of her office in the building they'd vacated for their new quarters. Blake's Brews had outgrown the converted silk-screen factory where Blake had started his enterprise just a few years ago. The bulk of the move had taken place over the past week, but the spacious new building just west of the airport was still a jungle of unpacked cartons and unhung paintings. Or, more accurately, it had been a jungle until that morning, when Blake had asked for volunteers willing to spend their Saturday helping to turn the place into a real home for the company.

Naturally, Martha had volunteered. What else did she have to do on a brisk October Saturday? She might have taken her mutt, Lucy, for a romp on the beach. She might have replenished her food supply and run a load of laundry. She might have raked the leaves from her yard. She might have taken a long bike ride—and she did, directly to the new building.

She would have biked home if Blake hadn't decided that it was too late for her to be safe on her two-wheeler. At around five o'clock, with the hallways fi-

nally clear of cartons and the chairs distributed into
the correct offices, Blake had announced that he was
going to order some pizzas, and anyone who wanted
to stick around to hang planters in the entry and set up
the pool table, the microwave oven, and the TV and
VCR in the employee lounge could have some slices
on him. Half the volunteers had departed, claiming
they had other plans. Martha never had plans. She'd
stayed.

At eight, when the Velcro dartboard had finally
been hung on the far wall of the lounge and the last of
the coffee supplies had been stored on the cabinet
shelf, she and the other stragglers had congratulated
each other on a job well done and trudged out of the
building. Blake had seen Martha unlocking her bicycle
and sliding her helmet off the chain.

"Hey, you shouldn't be biking home at this hour,"
he'd said.

"It's not that late."

"It's dark."

"I've got reflectors." She'd shown him the rear and
wheel reflectors, the headlight, the iridescent silver
strips on her helmet. "I'll be fine."

"Let me give you a lift home. I can wedge your bike
into the back seat. How about it?"

Why she should consider getting a lift home from
Blake Robey such a nerve-racking experience puzzled
her. He wasn't the best driver she'd ever ridden with,
but he wasn't the worst, either. He seemed a little
tired—it had been a long day of hard work, after all—
but his mood was cheerful. He wasn't knocking himself out to get a conversation going with her, which
was just as well, since ninety-five percent of their conversations revolved around the company's finances,

and she really didn't care to talk shop on a Saturday night.

She suppressed a scowl. Not wanting to talk shop had nothing to do with the day or the time. It had to do with her being alone in a car with Blake, with the top down and the sky above them sprayed with stars. It had to do with the fact that, while he was dressed in his standard office attire—faded jeans and a navy-blue T-shirt—she was also dressed in jeans rather than her typical work apparel—a subdued dress or pleated trousers and a silk blouse. She realized this was the first time Blake had seen her in blue jeans.

As if he gave a hoot what she wore.

"God, I'm wiped," he muttered, then yawned. She was obviously dazzling him with her scintillating conversational skills, wasn't she.

"You didn't have to drive me home," Martha said.

"Hey, you did me a big favor, sticking around so late. I appreciate it. I turn here, right?"

"Left," she said, then realized he'd meant the other definition of *right*. "Right."

"Left or right?" he asked, slowing and shooting her a grin.

He had dimples. He might have considered it too dark for a person to bike safely, but it wasn't too dark for Martha to see his dimples.

She simply couldn't fathom why she was so smitten with him. It wasn't as if he were a rock star, or someone she'd admired from afar for years. He was an amiable guy—friendly and easygoing although a bit too freewheeling for her peace of mind. But that was why he'd hired her. He was an idea man, a bartender who had stumbled upon his own unique recipes for fresh fruit smoothies and found a couple of investors willing to bankroll him when he decided to market Blake's Brews beyond the limited population of the beachside resort where he used to mix drinks at the waterfront bar. He thought big, dreamed bigger and laughed his way through the inevitable calamities entailed in starting a new business.

Martha was not a risk taker, and she didn't find humor in disasters. In fact, the most impulsive thing she had ever done in her life was to accept the job as accountant for Blake's and quit her drab, dependable position in Boston. To this day, she wasn't sure where she'd found the nerve to do it.

"That's my house," she said, pointing to the tidy shingled cottage she'd been lucky enough to discover for sale just days before she was scheduled to start working at Blake's Brews. It was a classic Cape Codder, an unpretentious box with a sloped roof, four rooms downstairs and two upstairs. Given the house's compact dimensions, it had been grossly overpriced, but it was south of Route 28, which meant it was close to the beach. People paid a premium for south-of-28 houses. Martha knew how to budget her money so she could afford it.

She'd liked its cozy size—less floor to vacuum, less air to heat in the winter—and its vest-pocket yard— less lawn to mow. She'd especially liked the screened back porch off the kitchen. Lucy liked the porch, too. She often spent her days there, running its length, drinking from her water dish and yapping at the seagulls and squirrels who perched on the wood rail that flanked the steps leading down to the yard.

Martha listened for Lucy's bark as Blake slowed the car to a halt alongside the grassy edge of the road. As soon as he turned off the engine, she heard the familiar sound, a couple of quick, lively yips. Poor girl. She'd been penned up all day. Martha would take her for a nice long walk as soon as Blake was gone.

He turned off the engine and shot her another quick smile. "Thanks," she said, turning from him to open her door. He opened his, too, and for a horrified moment she thought he might be considering walking her to her door—as if this were a date and he was hoping for a good-night kiss.

Fat chance of that. His only intention, she quickly saw, was to hoist her bicycle out of the back seat for her. It was reasonably light, but he lifted it as if it were weightless, gripping the crossbar and keeping his arm bent so the handlebars came even with his jaw. "Where do you want this?"

"Oh—just put it down," she said. "I can take care of it."

"That's all right. Tell me where you want it."

She had a detached garage behind the house, but as long as the weather was mild she kept the bike on her porch. "Around the back," she said, deciding she had no reason to argue. "Let me just get my other things." She reached into the rear seat for her helmet and backpack, then straightened up and smiled at him. If he accompanied her all the way to the back porch, should she invite him inside? Offer him a drink?

She didn't think she could handle having him in her house. Her nervous system was under enough strain just leading him across the front yard and up the unpaved driveway that led past the house to the garage. She heard Lucy bark as they approached; she heard the tapping of Lucy's paws against the floor as she scampered around, too excited to wait patiently.

"I've got a dog," she said to warn Blake as she

climbed the three steps ahead of him and unlatched the door. Turning, she found Blake at the bottom of the steps, frowning. "I keep the bike on the porch until it's too cold to use it," she said, assuming he was confused about where to leave it.

She eased open the door, bracing herself for Lucy's exuberant welcome. The dog leaped at her, yelping and panting with delight, a bundle of fur and limbs and a long, pink tongue. Martha dropped her helmet and pack on the lounge chair near the door and scooped Lucy up off the floor so she wouldn't fling herself at Blake. With a family tree that featured assorted terrier breeds, Lucy wasn't huge, but she probably weighed more than the bicycle. And when she was wired, as she was now, she could easily knock over even someone as tall and solidly built as Blake, if he wasn't expecting her to leap at him.

He obviously wasn't. As he climbed the steps, he stared at her and her energetic pooch, a bemused smile curving his lips. "Hey, there," he said, propping the bike against the wall and reaching out to scratch Lucy behind the ears. Lucy twisted her head so she could lick his hand.

"Her name is Lucy," Martha told him, cradling the dog in her arms. As Blake continued to scratch Lucy, she calmed down, moving her head to afford him access to the underside of her chin. She panted happily. Martha supposed that if she were Lucy, getting rubbed and patted by Blake, she'd be panting happily, too.

Stupid thought. Her cheeks felt hot, despite the cool night air. Blake was standing awfully close to her as he stroked the nape of Lucy's neck. He was close enough that Martha could see the golden hairs on his forearms in the amber glow of the porch light. She could see the day's growth of beard along his jaw. She could smell the faint traces of his spicy shampoo. "Hey, there, Lucy," he cooed. "How's it going, girl?" Martha could almost feel his breath on her face.

She could almost feel his gaze on her face, too, and when she stole a glance at him, she realized he was staring at her. Staring as if something was wrong—as if she had a smear of ink on her cheek, or maybe she'd grown a second nose. "What?" she asked.

"I never would have figured you for a dog."

She must have looked perplexed, because he elaborated. "You seem more like a cat type."

A cat type. Translation: a single woman. Why did people always assume single women favored cats? Especially plain spinsters and feminists—and Martha conceded that it wouldn't be a huge stretch to apply either of those labels to her. She also happened to believe that on average, cats were smarter than dogs—she'd be the first to admit that Lucy could be a bimbo. But she hadn't adopted Lucy for the dog's brains. She'd adopted her because she'd seen her photo in a free community newspaper a year ago, accompanied by a blurb from the local animal shelter stating that this lovely puppy and many other dogs like her needed good homes. Lucy had looked so heart-meltingly adorable in the photo, Martha hadn't been able to resist.

It was oddly similar to the impulsive way she'd accepted Blake's offer of a job. She'd seen his adorable face and her heart had melted.

She looked at his adorable face now. He was giving Lucy a two-handed rubdown along her ribs and back, and the dog was in ecstasy, her eyes closed and her tongue dripping saliva onto the floorboards. Of course Blake would be a dog person. He had floppy hair, too, and expressive eyes, and he seemed like the sort whose idea of nirvana was a full-body massage.

"Nice place you've got," he commented, continuing to stroke Lucy while he gazed at his surroundings. Martha had decorated the porch with a serviceable glass-topped table and padded chairs, and the lounge chair with matching upholstery. Besides the simple furnishings and the yellow lightbulb above the door, there wasn't much to see. It was too dark for him to make out her backyard, but even in broad daylight it wasn't impressive: grass, a hedge of lilacs bordering the southern edge of the lot, the detached garage, a dwarf pine tree and another hedge of lilacs bordering the northern edge. Even if she knew much about gardening, she wouldn't have had a chance to do any landscaping, since she'd moved into the house in late summer.

The interior of her house wasn't spectacular, either. The rooms were small, and she'd managed to arrange her furniture in them in an appealing manner, but if Blake ever saw her kitchen or living room, what would probably impress him most was their neatness. Martha wasn't compulsive, but she approached housekeeping the way she approached accounting: everything placed precisely where it belonged so that the totality was correct. Martha's sister Nancy had a flair for decorating, but she lived in the Washington D.C. area. She'd promised to help Martha fix the place up the next time she visited, but that probably wouldn't be until next summer. The big holidays had to be spent at their parents' house in Connecticut.

Nancy wouldn't have time to detour to the Cape over Thanksgiving or Christmas.

For now, Martha didn't mind the lack of stylishness in her home. It suited her well enough, and it left Lucy free to run around without doing serious damage.

"She's getting heavy," Martha murmured as Lucy slipped into a semiconscious trance in her arms. "I've got to put her down."

"Here, let me," Blake said simultaneously, sliding his hands under Lucy as Martha started to lower her. Her shoulder collided with his, and his hand slid over her wrist as he lifted the dog from her arms. Just that one brush of his fingers against her skin made her understand why Lucy looked so blissful. His palm was as dry as hers had been damp during the drive home, and his fingertips felt smooth and confident. She wanted to close her eyes, to imagine the feel of those fingertips against her cheek.

Oh, for heaven's sake! Martha was an intelligent, self-aware woman who saved her wild imaginings only for private moments, when no one could witness her foolishness—and no one could interrupt it with a cold dose of reality.

There was plenty of reality on the screened porch right now, in the form of Blake himself. The actual man was never going to touch his fingertips to her cheek. What he was going to do was lower her dog to the ground and say good night, maybe after thanking her once more for her assistance in getting the company's new headquarters up and running.

The moment he lowered Lucy, she roused herself, stretched and embarked on a vigorous olfactory inspection of his sneakers. "Do you have a dog?" Martha asked, wondering whether Lucy smelled a rival on the scuffed white leather.

"Not at the moment." He ignored Lucy as she sniffed his feet and scampered around his ankles. A gust of wind filtered through the screens and wrapped around Martha, chilling her. The end of October leaned more toward winter than summer on the Cape, and she hugged her arms around herself for warmth. "Well, anyway," Blake said, "I guess I'll be heading off."

"Thanks for the ride," she said.

"Thanks for helping out today."

"No problem."

He eyed her dog for a moment, then hesitated by the steps and frowned. "I'm trying to remember something," he said vaguely.

"Something about the move today? Or something in the books?" Great. She was talking like an accountant again, reminding Blake of exactly who and what she was—as if he would ever forget.

"No, something else." Lucy zeroed in on his left foot, circling it and then sitting on it. "Something about tonight. Something was supposed to happen."

You were supposed to sweep me into your arms, instead of Lucy, Martha fantasized. *You were supposed to look into my eyes and say, "Good God, Martha! I never realized how sexy you were!"* She had to bite her lip to keep from snorting at her runaway imagination.

"Something I've got to do..." He frowned.

"The Good Earth account?" she suggested, mentioning a Chicago-based health food chain that was on the verge of adding Blake's Fruit Brews to its inventory.

"Daylight saving," he remembered, curling his

hand into a fist and rapping it gently against his fore-head. "We're supposed to reset our clocks tonight."

"Oh that's right." Martha nodded. She would have remembered when she went indoors—the morning newspaper had carried a reminder on the front page.

"So, remind me, do we go forward or backward?"

"Spring ahead, fall back," she recited. "We have to set our clocks back an hour. We get an extra hour of sleep tonight."

"Or we can stay up an extra hour," he said with a playful smile. She saw his dimples again. She couldn't *not* see his dimples. Long after he left, long after she took Lucy for a final walk and then went inside, show-ered and put on her pajamas and snuggled down in her bed, she would still be seeing his dimples.

Martha was willing to bet that if he stayed up an ex-tra hour tonight, he'd spend that hour doing some-thing more interesting than lying in bed thinking about the dimples of someone who wasn't with him.

"You know, daylight saving doesn't officially end until 2:00 a.m.," he said. "I always wondered about that. Who decided on 2:00 a.m.?"

"You're supposed to reset the clocks before you go to bed," she explained.

He gave her an exaggerated look of comprehension. "Oh, we are? Gee, I was planning on staying awake till two and changing the clocks then. I wouldn't want to cheat and set them before the whole thing actually happened."

His sarcasm made her acknowledge how idiotic she must have sounded. "Sorry," she said, gazing down at Lucy, who seemed uncommonly comfortable sitting on his instep.

"Hey, no." He laughed, a sound much warmer than

the whisper of the breeze through the screens. "One of these days I'm going to stay up till two, though. Just to see what happens to that hour. You know? We lose it every spring, we get it back every fall.... Where do you think it goes between spring and fall?"

Puzzled, she scrutinized him in the amber light. Was he teasing her, or did he really not understand the principle behind daylight savings? Or was he waxing philosophical? Existential curiosity was something she certainly didn't expect of a former bartender who seemed much more interested in the nuances of flavor that differentiated white grape juice from purple grape juice, or the relative merits of glass bottles over plastic, than about the meaning of Time.

He seemed to be expecting an answer from her. "It doesn't go anywhere," she said. "It just—it's like bookkeeping. You subtract it from one column and add it to another. Then, at the end of the accounting period, you shift it back."

His smile grew even more playful, almost wicked. It ignited sapphire lights in his eyes. "I think that hour is just out there, waiting for us to reclaim it, you know? It's our time, it got stolen from us last spring, and now we're getting it back. And since it's extra, we can do whatever we want with it. Kind of like a bonus." He held her gaze with his for a moment, then shrugged and slid his foot gently out from under Lucy. "Or maybe like a gift. It's ours until we have to give it back next spring. What do you think, Martha? It would be a shame to waste a gift like that."

"Waste it?" He definitely was wandering in a more philosophical direction than she could grasp. "It's an hour in the middle of the night—when we're supposed to be asleep."

"It's a bonus," he insisted. "I plan to make the most of it—and I think you should, too." With that, he turned and headed down the steps. She watched through the screen door as the night swallowed him in its shadows.

MARTHA COOPER HAD A DOG?

Blake wasn't sure why that should be such a shock to him. The truth was, he'd never really thought of Martha Cooper in the context of pets. Or a bike, or a house...or a life.

Martha was Martha. She'd appeared in his office last July, the answer to his dreams. He hadn't cared who she was or where she'd come from or what her astrological sign was—or whether she had a dog. All that had mattered was that she was an accountant, she could unravel the tangled figures in his books, she could make sense of data in computers, she could count to twenty without having to remove her shoes— and she was willing to work for Blake's Brews.

He'd been desperate. The company had grown bigger than he'd ever imagined, faster than he'd planned for it, and suddenly there were regional distributors to deal with, and advertising, and all kinds of business stuff that Blake had never given much thought to when he'd been blending fruit smoothies for fun and selling them for a small profit. There were big profits now, and payroll and health plans for employees. He'd hired a human resources director, and she'd told him he'd sure as hell better hire a numbers person, too.

His ad hadn't exactly brought in a stampede of applicants. On the Cape in July, the only people thinking about work were college kids looking for the kind of jobs that wouldn't tax their brains—chambermaids, waitresses, gift-shop clerks. He'd gotten only three responses to his ad. The first had been a spoiled rich Harvard graduate who had talked as if he had marshmallows stuffed into his sinuses and had acted so patronizing that Blake had had to suppress the urge to punch the guy in his orthodontically perfect teeth. The second applicant had been a chipper grandmother who had been a bookkeeper for forty years at her husband's grocery store and didn't know a thing about computers.

The third had been Martha Cooper. Quiet, competent Martha. No-muss, no-fuss Martha. Steady and sober, Martha operated at one speed—efficient—and at one volume—muted. She didn't bother him; she didn't badger him. She was just *there,* making sure everything that needed to be done got done.

But he never would have pegged her as a dog person. He'd considered her kind of old-maidish, and he tended to associate old maids with cats, or maybe parakeets. Now that he'd seen Martha with her dog, however, he was going to have to rethink everything.

He liked surprises. He liked getting walloped by the unexpected. It was an adventure, having to consider someone from an entirely new perspective.

Actually, he'd never considered Martha from any perspective, old or new. But all of a sudden, there he'd been, petting her dog and babbling about daylight saving time with her. Before now, the most interesting conversation they'd ever shared had been about which store sold the best bagels in town. He'd recommended a place out toward South Yarmouth on Route 28, and Roger in product development had insisted that some ritzy, pricy bakery in town was better. Martha had mentioned that where she'd used to live, in Brookline, there had been numerous kosher delis, so she counted herself as something of a connoisseur when it came to bagels.

It had been nice of her to help out today. She hadn't eaten as much pizza as Roger and Doug and the office managers, but she was kind of on the scrawny side; maybe she just wasn't a big eater. Blake had assumed she was the type who would favor dry toast and tea with lemon for breakfast, or maybe high-fiber cereal with skim milk. He had no idea what she ate for lunch—he'd see her sometimes in the lounge with a brown bag, but he never paid attention to what she was unpacking from it. Plain yogurt would be his guess.

He ought to stop making assumptions about her. Martha clearly had a few surprises up her sleeve. A dog, of all things. A dog named Lucy.

He reached downtown Hyannis. On a Saturday night in the off season, the place was eerily tranquil, all the summer folks gone, the roads relatively clear of traffic and the sidewalks unclogged. Blake had grown up on the Cape, and he knew its seasonal rhythms. Like most natives, he'd learned to appreciate the vacationers who crowded onto the Cape all summer long, pouring their money into the local economy, but he'd also learned that that narrow arm of land reaching out into the Atlantic and brandishing its fist in Boston's direction was a much nicer place once all those vacationers emptied their wallets and went home.

He was going home, too. Most Saturday nights would find him with a party, somewhere to go, someone to go with. But he was tired tonight, not just from the physical labor of lugging furniture and hanging pictures throughout the new building but also from the mental stress of accepting that his company was growing beyond his fledgling dreams for it. Not just growing—growing up. The move to the new building was only the latest evidence that Blake's Fruit Brews had flourished into something real, something ambitious, something—God help him—*corporate*.

That was an incredibly tiring thought.

But he'd have an extra hour tonight to recover from the shock that Blake Robey, fun-loving goof-off extraordinaire, had become a mogul. If he was shocked that his accountant had a dog, he was just as shocked that he was running a major company on the verge of expanding its market beyond New England. Talk about getting walloped by the unexpected—Blake had somehow managed to wallop himself with his own success.

IT WAS A TYPICAL Saturday night for Martha—almost. Typical in that she gave Lucy a long walk, then took a bath, then donned her cotton pj's, curled up with a bowl of ice cream and watched TV, and by eleven was struggling to keep her eyes open. But it was atypical because, before she could retire to bed, she had to reset the clocks.

It was at times like this—daylight saving, or after a power outage, that she was forced to acknowledge how very many clocks she owned. The wall clock in the kitchen, the clock built into the oven, the clock on the microwave, the timer clock on the coffeemaker. In the den, the clock programmed into the TV and the clock programmed into the VCR. Upstairs, the clock in the guest bedroom, her wristwatch, her alarm clock.

She sat on the edge of her bed, stared at the electronic clock radio on her nightstand, and wondered about that extra hour.

Where did it go? Where did it come from?

How was Blake going to spend that hour?

A guy like him? Ha. She could guess.

She plumped her pillow, turned down the cover, and slid between the cool linen sheets. A man like Blake Robey would not be sliding between the sheets alone on a Saturday night. She knew he wasn't married, and the office scuttlebutt implied that he wasn't seriously involved with anyone, but Martha couldn't help believing that he would have no difficulty finding someone to warm his bed.

Would they be staying awake until 2:00 a.m. to see where the extra hour came from?

She laughed at the absurdity of that. But when she reached for her alarm clock to reset the time, her hand seemed to defy her. Her fingers fumbled onto the wrong button, accidentally turning on the radio and filling her bedroom with the melancholy lilt of a Bonnie Raitt ballad.

Maybe she wouldn't reset this clock, after all. Maybe she'd stay awake until 2:00 a.m, then turn back the time and indulge in her bonus hour, if she had enough energy. If she didn't, no harm done. Tomorrow was Sunday. She could sleep as late as she wanted.

She lifted her hand to the lamp and switched it off. The room fell dark, except for the glowing red digits on her clock. Bonnie Raitt grieved that she couldn't make her man love her. The song made Martha feel even more alone, but she couldn't bring herself to turn the radio off.

Another song came on, another ballad. Another lament about love lost, love never had, love longed for. Closing her eyes, Martha recalled how Blake had leaned toward her on the porch, his hand brushing hers as he lifted Lucy from her arms. She pictured his shimmering eyes, his dimples, his long, lean body so close to hers.

Still thinking of him, she drifted off to the crooning of yet another lovelorn singer. The night closed snugly around her as she slept, and the music drifted into the air, a soulful lullaby.

And then it stopped. The abrupt silence jarred her awake. She opened her eyes and saw the glowing digits on her clock—2:00 a.m.

A shadow crossed her line of vision, reaching across the radio, touching a button to change the time to one o'clock.

Someone was in her room. Someone had turned off her radio and reset her clock. Someone was standing right beside her bed.

She pleaded for her eyes to adjust to the darkness, pleaded for her heart to keep beating steadily so she wouldn't faint. She pleaded for whoever it was, whoever had broken into her house, gotten past Lucy, climbed her stairs and stolen into her bedroom to leave without hurting her. He could take what he wanted—her money, her jewelry, all her appliances with their built-in reset clocks. But please, she silently begged, please don't hurt her or her dog.

The shadow began to take shape. Tall, lanky, a man's silhouette. He didn't move.

"Who's there?" she whispered, clutching her blanket to her chin. Her voice sounded steadier than her pulse, which thumped painfully in her head. "What do you want?"

"I'm your gift," he whispered back, his voice unrecognizable. "It's your hour, and here I am."

2

MARTHA WAS DREAMING. She had to be. If she wasn't dreaming, she would be scared out of her mind, and she wasn't.

This was her bonus. It didn't count in real time. This hour had been stolen six months ago, in April, and now it was being returned to her to do with as she wished.

Her bedroom was too dark for her to see the intruder's face, too silent to hear anything but his steady breathing and her own wild pulse. "What do you want?" she asked, a breathless edge in her voice.

"You." Just that one word. It should have sent her screaming and charging for the door. But instead, it reassured her, offering her one more bit of proof that this was a dream.

He revealed himself only as a silhouette. She couldn't see his eyes, his mouth, his chest. He appeared to be naked from the waist up, the outline of his torso sharply visible, a sculpture of streamlined muscle. Above the horizontal line of his shoulders, his face remained shadowed. His hair looked mussed, falling nearly to his shoulders. She wondered whether it had gotten windblown when he'd entered her house—or perhaps before he'd entered her house— say, from driving around in a convertible car.

She wondered *how* he'd entered her house. Had he

climbed through a window? Why hadn't Lucy barked?

It was a dream, she reminded herself. How he'd gained entry didn't matter. All that mattered was that he was here, and it was her hour.

She moved her gaze back down to his chest, hesitating before she reached his waist. She couldn't be sure, but it looked as if he had on snug-fitting jeans.

A bare-chested man in tight jeans was standing in her bedroom at 2:00 a.m. Or 1:00 a.m. Or some non-existent hour in between.

And he wanted her.

He loomed above her, moving closer to the bed. Suddenly she wasn't so sure it was a dream, after all. Fear nipped at her—but not fear that he'd hurt her. He was her gift, for her hour, and none of this was really happening...yet she couldn't shake off her alarm. She had never had *this* kind of dream before. She wasn't sure how the dream was supposed to go, what she was supposed to do in it.

"Don't be afraid," he whispered. How did he know she was afraid? Good God, could he read her mind? That made him even more dangerous.

He took another step and rested one knee on the mattress, causing it to slope. Gravity drew her toward him, and her hand brushed against his leg. She recognized the texture of denim. Tight jeans, all right.

Shifting, he slid his leg forward and lowered himself onto the bed. She wished he would speak so she could hear his voice and perhaps identify it. Even if he was a dream, she wanted to know who this man of her dreams was.

Hell. She knew who he was—the same man she'd been dreaming about since a spur-of-the-moment interview had landed her a new job last July. She knew whose hair was just that length, whose shoulders were just that width. If she closed her eyes, she would probably be able to visualize his dimples, even though she still couldn't see his face.

This was her dream, and it was her hour. She was allowed to enjoy it. "Don't waste it," Blake had told her.

All right. She wouldn't waste it. But how to make the most of it? She wasn't exactly worldly; she'd had pathetically little experience with men, in or out of bed, and the few men she'd dated in her life had been decidedly safe and staid. They had never appeared full-blown and seminaked in her middle-of-the-night fantasies. If they had, she would have awakened herself and kept blinking until they disappeared.

The men she dated were not the stuff of dreams. They were...well, the sort of men who would go for a reticent woman of mediocre looks who derived satisfaction from crunching numbers. Martha knew who and what she was, and if she ever felt a compelling need to get married, she would marry one of those mild, compatible men and make as happy a life as she could with him.

She assumed she would recognize a need to settle down when she was ready to give up fantasizing about utterly inappropriate men—like Blake. Or like this shadowy stranger.

"Don't be afraid," he whispered again. If he spoke with his full voice, she might be able to recognize it and identify him. But perhaps it was just as well he remained anonymous. He was reminding her enough of Blake to make her pulse jagged.

He brushed a strand of her hair off her cheek, his

fingertips trailing heat on her skin, a heat that soaked into her, seeped down through her body and settled in her soul. If she had a little more nerve, she would have touched him. But she was panicked. He could tell her as many times as he wanted not to be afraid, but she would feel whatever she felt, no matter what he said. She would feel anxious and insecure and...warm. Hot.

He ran his hand lightly over her face, tracing her eyebrows, her nose from bridge to tip, her upper lip, her lower lip. Along the edge of her chin to her temple, her ear. She wondered if he was unable to see her face the way she was unable to see his. She wondered if a figment of her imagination had the ability to see at all, or if he was stroking her the way a blind person might stroke a face, trying to visualize it with his fingertips. She wondered if he had the ability to feel what she was feeling with each caress.

She wondered when his other hand was going to join in. And when—*if*—she was going to find the courage to touch him.

One question was answered when he lifted his free hand to the edge of the blanket she was clutching in front of her like a shield. He eased it out of her grip and let it fall down into her lap, then brought his hand to her shoulder. He would probably think her pajamas were childish, she thought with mild dismay. She had never owned an elegant negligee, a gown of gossamer silk that would spill sensuously over her body, outlining her breasts and her hips and whispering against her skin.

He didn't comment on the pajamas, though. He only traced her shoulder through the cotton, down as far as her elbow and then back up again to the rounded neckline. His fingers grazed her throat and she heard herself sigh.

Oh, what a dream this was turning out to be. What an hour. What a gift.

Her legs moved of their own volition, causing the blanket to ripple. Her hips felt restless and her heart pounded faster, harder. She wanted him to touch her throat again. She wanted him to twirl his fingers through her hair, behind her ears, down to the nape of her neck. Why couldn't she just make it happen by dreaming it? Why couldn't she force her dream to go exactly where she wanted?

Maybe it was better if she just gave herself over to it, letting anticipation build inside her like water behind a dam, a delicious pressure that would burst forth when the time was right. She ordered herself to relax, to enjoy the moment and not strain to get ahead of her dream man. His light, seemingly aimless caresses felt wonderful all by themselves. She was going to trust him to continue making her feel wonderful. Even if she couldn't direct the dream, she knew it was *her* dream, and he was *her* gift, and nothing was going to go wrong here. If it did, she would simply wake up.

She sank back into the pillows and he followed her down, combing his hands through her hair, warming her cheeks with his palms before he slid both hands down to the top button of her pajamas. He popped it open and her heart lurched. He popped the next button open, and the next, and her hips clenched. She wanted to talk to him, to tell him to move faster, to slow down and wait for her to catch up—but no. She had decided to let the dream unfold on its own, not to fight it or push it but instead to let it carry her.

She didn't really want to talk, anyway. She didn't

want to hear his voice and realize that it didn't belong to Blake Robey. Let him remain her shadow lover, anonymous and universal. Let him be anyone in the world, anyone she wanted. Right now she wanted no one but him.

He opened the final button and spread apart the fabric to expose her breasts. Slowly, agonizingly slowly, he skimmed his hands upward from her waist, his thumbs meeting above her navel. She was thin, small-chested, but in her dream she knew the size of her bosom was not going to be an issue. He wasn't going to comment, as one unintentionally insulting fellow she'd dated in college had, that when she lay on her back her ribs protruded higher than her breasts. She'd been fully clothed at the time—and after he'd made that observation, she'd decided the jerk would never see her in any state other than fully clothed.

But the shadow man wasn't going to speak, and he wasn't going to criticize. He was going to continue moving his hands up until they cupped her breasts, until his fingers arched around the soft flesh and then narrowed to pinch her nipples.

She moaned. It broke the silence in the room—her moan, her sharp breath, the quiet creak of her bedsprings as he rose completely onto the bed and kneaded her breasts. She couldn't hear him breathing, or moaning, or even moving. She still couldn't see his face. All she could do was feel him—which was really more than enough.

He bowed toward her and touched his lips to her forehead. A gentle kiss, like a benediction—yet it was unbearably erotic. Her hips grew heavy; her toes curled. She craned her neck, offering him her mouth.

He ignored it, choosing instead to kiss her eyelids,

the bridge of her nose, the outer edge of her cheek-
bone, the fringe of hair at her temple. He kissed the
sharp line of her jaw, a surprisingly sensitive spot of
skin below her ear, the base of her throat. All the while
his hands continued their exploration of her breasts.
Slowly. So slowly she couldn't bear it, but if he sped
up or stopped it would be even more unbearable.

Her breath grew ragged. She parted her lips, hoping
to draw in desperately needed oxygen—and then he
crushed his mouth to hers, sliding his tongue deep.
The sensation was so intense, her entire body shud-
dered in delight.

She'd never felt anything like this before. She'd
never *wanted* anything like this. She'd never known
she was capable of dreaming it.

Her mouth moved with his, danced with his. His
kiss gave her the courage to wrap her arms around
him. His back was warm and smooth, as if it had been
baked by the sun through a long Cape Cod summer.
She felt his muscles flexing beneath the skin, felt the
solid bones of his shoulders, felt the weight of him as
he shifted again, stretching to lie beside her.

Her legs wanted his. She kicked futilely at the blanket, then realized he was lying on top of it, pinning it
so she couldn't kick it off. She wanted to protest but he
was kissing her too deeply. She wanted to shove the
blanket down with her hands, but that would mean
letting go of him and she couldn't bring herself to do
that.

What kisses. What heaven. Her limited history with
men had included, besides that oaf who'd ridiculed
her tiny breasts, several men who'd confused passion
with force and considered it the height of seduction to

smash her lips against her teeth until her entire mouth was sore.

Not this man. Of course not. His kiss was hard but finessed, only hinting at the possibility of domination. His tongue possessed the inner recesses of her mouth, but then allowed her tongue to overtake him, to tease and parry and subdue him. It was a give-and-take, not only a take.

She loved it. She loved it so much that when he pulled back she almost cried out in protest. But she bit her lip—tasting him on it, a minty male flavor—and let him continue to do what he was doing.

What he was doing was lifting her to sit, just enough so he could slide the pajama top down her arms and toss it aside. Then he lowered her back to the pillows and, at last, freed her legs from their imprisonment beneath the blanket. He tugged the drawstring at the waist of her pajama bottoms. When it went slack, he pulled them off, so smoothly they almost felt like elegant silk on her skin.

She should have been bashful, sprawled out naked before this stranger. But this was a dream, and his kiss had stripped away her inhibitions as easily as his hands had stripped away her pajamas. If he hadn't criticized her breasts, he probably wasn't going to criticize the rest of her, either.

She wouldn't let him. She could control that much of her dream, at least. Maybe not the speed or the direction of it, but she could will away any aspects that would bruise her ego.

So he would think she was beautiful. He would think she was slender, not thin, and he would think her hair was lush and luxuriant, worthy of that overpriced haircut she'd gotten. He would think her eyes were the color of dark chocolate, not mud, and her fingers were dainty, not stubby. He would think she was magnificent, the sexiest woman in the world.

He skimmed his hands down from her hips to her thighs, to her knees, her calves, her insteps. He stroked the soles of her feet. His playful caresses tickled, but she swallowed her laughter. He touched each toe, lavishing a little extra attention on her big toes. In her scenario, he wasn't going to notice the calluses rimming her heels. He was going to think her feet were unspeakably beautiful.

She reached down and her hands filled with his hair. It was as soft and lush as she'd wished her own hair was. Did Blake's hair feel so soft?

Tonight it did, she told herself. Tonight, buffeted by the sea breezes as he'd driven his Mustang through town, his hair had been conditioned by the wind and the moon, and now she could feel the wind and the moon in each strand of this stranger's hair.

He abandoned her feet, and she heard the hiss of a zipper being opened, then the rustle of his jeans being shed. Another brief bout of panic seized her, and she fought it off.

She reached down again and this time touched his shoulder. He rose above her, all darkness and heat, graceful and virile, frightening yet welcome. She let her hands roam the breadth of his shoulders, feeling the rugged bone and sinew that shaped his upper body.

She toyed with the ends of his hair and tried to imagine Blake's smile, his devilish dimples. But if she'd had an opportunity to glimpse the stranger's face, it vanished when he bowed to kiss her breasts. First one and then the other, back and forth, he tasted them, nipped and licked and tugged on them with his lips. As his tongue bathed her skin, waves of bliss bathed her soul. She sighed and ran her fingers through his hair again, holding his head to her.

He eased out of her reach, sliding downward, kissing downward. He touched his tongue to her navel, kissed the twin points of her pelvis, slid lower and pressed his mouth between her legs. She *couldn't* be dreaming this, because she'd never even dared to think about it. But it was happening to her now, her gift, and her entire body seemed to squeeze tight, as if clinging to the feeling, refusing to relax because if she did, the excruciating pleasure of it might slip away.

Her hips rose to him. Her hands fisted. Her breath escaped from her in uneven gasps as his fingers found her, and then his tongue, and then his fingers again. Her thighs strained against him; her eyes squeezed shut and her heart stopped beating for an endless moment. And then everything broke loose inside her, a raging pulse of heat overtaking her.

She inhaled, forced her fingers to unfurl and opened her eyes. He was still there, kneeling between her legs, planting a gentle kiss on her belly as her body unwound.

What a dream, she thought dazedly. Oh, lord, what a dream. She never, ever wanted to wake up.

She turned to glance at her clock radio. No red digits glowed on its surface. Maybe her hour wasn't over yet.

When she turned back, her vision filled with the shadow of him rising up above her. He gathered one of her hands in his, kissed her thumb, and then guided her down to his erection. He kept his hand closed around hers, letting her learn him, feel him, stroke him. Would he gasp for breath the way she had? she wondered. Could he feel what she was feeling? She wanted him to. Whoever or whatever he was, she wanted him to be as transported by this as she was.

She brought her other hand down, touching his thighs, his abdomen, the wiry nest of hair below. She listened for him to groan, listened for any indication that she was having an effect on him. There was one obvious indication, of course, but she wanted more than a simple biological reflex. She wanted him insane for her, rapturous, overwhelmed by her.

She rose off the pillow to kiss his neck. She wasn't as talented at kissing as he was, but she tried her best, re-calling every cinematic love scene she'd ever watched, every romantic novel she'd ever read—every kiss her dream man had given her that night. She used her tongue, her teeth, her lips on his chest, nibbling, graz-ing. He tasted salty and warm, heavenly.

Then she heard it, a low growl arising from some-where deep inside him. She'd gotten the response she wanted. She'd pushed him over some edge—if only she knew what edge it was.

He rolled over, onto his back, bringing her with him so she lay on top of him. That he was resting his head on her pillows dazzled her. Perhaps she would find a strand of his hair on the pillowcase in the morning. Perhaps she would smell him, see his imprint in the down, feel him against her cheek after he was gone. She let him arrange her above him, let him spread her legs around him and cup her hips and pull her down.

It had never been like this before, not for her. Never so sweet, never so fierce. Never, in her scant experi-ence, had a man's body fit hers so perfectly, sliding, surging, touching her in places she hadn't even known about, in ways she could barely fathom.

He kept one hand on her hips while the other glided up her back, warm and erotic, his fingertips running along her spine until he reached the nape of her neck. He squeezed lightly, sending a hot chill back down her spine along the route his hand had taken. She gasped and he thrust deeper, deeper, until she was lost, her body convulsing and her soul shattering.

She collapsed on top of him, faint with exhaustion and dizzy with joy. Beneath her she felt the rapid beat of his heart against her cheek, the final pulse of his climax between her legs. Had she pleased him? Was he as sated as she was?

Was it at all possible that *she* was *his* dream? That some man, some mysterious being whose identity she could only guess at, was dreaming about making love like this with Martha Cooper the accountant?

She'd never been a femme fatale and never would be—but maybe that was another dream of hers, along with her dreams of Blake Robey. Maybe the real dream was that she could be the kind of woman who would satisfy a man like Blake Robey in bed, that she could be the woman of his dreams.

That would never happen. This was *her* bonus. Somewhere across town or down the Cape, or wherever Blake happened to be at 2:00 a.m. on the night daylight saving ended, he was receiving his own bonus, indulging in his own dream. And his dream would have nothing to do with her, she was certain.

Sighing, she lifted herself off the man. She wished she could see his face just once, wished she could know for one fleeting instant who this glorious lover was. "How much longer do we have?" she asked.

"Look at the clock," he whispered.

She eased off him and twisted to view the clock radio's face. A faint red glow emanated from it, where the digits ought to have been, as if they were regaining strength after a power outage. Gradually, they clarified into the distinctive stick-figure electronic numerals she knew: 2:00.

She spun around.

The man was gone.

3

"BLAKE, you aren't listening to me," Doug Horowitz complained. Doug was Blake's vice president of marketing. He was smart, he had a bachelor's and a master's degree—which was two more degrees than Blake had—and under ordinary circumstances, Blake went out of his way to pay attention to anything Doug might have to say.

But that Monday morning wasn't ordinary. Blake was tired. He was restless. He was having a ridiculous amount of difficulty trying to focus, and he didn't know why.

He had a suspicion, though. Monday was giving him a serious challenge because the weekend had been so weird. He blamed the weirdness on daylight saving; apparently, he hadn't been able to adjust to the change in time.

Everything had seemed normal enough Saturday evening. He'd arrived home without incident, opened a beer—even the founder and owner of Blake's Fruit Brews sometimes wanted a *real* brew instead of a blended fruit smoothie on a Saturday night—found a football game on one of the cable sports stations and sprawled out on the sofa in his den. He'd emptied his mind of everything but the action on the TV screen and the sour tang of the beer on his tongue. He hadn't thought about the new building, his company's growth or Martha Cooper and her dog.

He'd stayed awake long enough to catch the eleven o'clock news, with its nagging reminder that viewers should turn their clocks back an hour before bed. He'd reset his clocks, then showered and crashed for the night.

But he hadn't slept well. All night long he would drift off, then awaken with a start—and with a hard-on. Like a kid, for crying out loud. He would keep falling asleep and dreaming...God, he didn't even know what he was dreaming, but whatever it was, it must have been triple-X-rated, because he'd suddenly find himself wide-awake and at full attention. The third time it happened, he'd gotten out of bed and taken another shower, just to cool off. Then he'd staggered back to bed, conked out...and jolted himself awake, out of breath and horny as hell.

Tense and crabby, he'd arisen too early on Sunday—and the clock had told him it was an hour earlier than too early. He'd spent the day aimlessly, puttering around the house, glowering at the steady drizzle leaking from the overcast sky and contemplating the acquisition of a dog. As if he really needed a dog in his life. As if owning a business wasn't enough responsibility for a guy who had never considered responsibility his long suit.

So here it was, Monday morning, and the person with the best brain for business strategy in the company was yakking at him about Chicago. He knew he ought to pay attention, but damn. Not now. Not when the world seemed out of whack.

"Good Earth Foods is a major, major market," Doug was saying. "I thought everything was a go with them, but all of a sudden they're hedging. I don't know what happened. A fax was waiting for me when I got into the office, saying they weren't ready to go to contract at this time. I called them right away, but I couldn't get a straight answer out of anyone—"

"Of course you couldn't. It's nine-thirty on a Monday morning. Which would make it, what? Seven-thirty there?"

Dough scowled. Even though he was Blake's age, he looked about ten years older. Maybe it was his precision-cut hair, maybe his precision-cut suit. Maybe it was all that scholarly wisdom in his eyes—or the stylish wire-rimmed glasses framing his eyes. "Look at a map, Blake," he scolded. "Chicago is not on Mountain Time."

"Who cares what time it's on? Nobody's on the right time, anyway. Daylight saving always screws everything up."

Doug gave Blake a look of pure exasperation. "I think our best move would be to go out to Chicago and talk to the Good Earth folks face-to-face. We've got to see with our own eyes what's going on there. They were so gung ho about the product as recently as a month ago, a week ago—and all of a sudden, they're mumbling about shelf space and advertising commitments. They pride themselves on promoting healthful eating, but what do you want to bet we're competing with soda for the space?"

"Bottled water," Blake disputed him. "Everybody thinks bottled water is the primo health drink. They should look at a drop of water under a microscope sometime. It's full of little squishy swimming things. Amoebas and germs and stuff." He remembered his fascination with all those busy one-cell critters when he'd studied water under a microscope in a high school biology class. The girl sharing the microscope with him had screamed and gagged and made retching noises, but Blake had thought it was pretty cool. Not exactly healthy-looking, though.

"Anyway, I still think we need to plan a trip out there, and pronto. If you want, I can go alone—but I think you could add a lot to a meeting. We can't send anyone lower than me, though. Gloria or Will would be great, but they just don't have the leverage. They'll get shuffled off onto low-level management and we'll never get this situation turned around."

Doug had too much energy. He was like a too bright sun or a too strong wind; his mere existence made Blake's head ache. "Sure," he said. "You can go to Chicago and fix the problem."

"I think it would be more effective if you came, too," Doug added. "You were the one who landed the deal in the first place."

Blake opened his mouth and then closed it. He'd landed the deal because he'd met the daughter of the owner of the Good Earth health food chain at a resort in Jamaica and they'd hit it off. He and Tracy had had a dandy time for a week, and she'd insisted that her father would love to carry his product. They'd managed to e-mail back and forth a few times when they'd returned to the States, but then she'd told him she had decided it was time to get married, and she'd found the right fellow to do that with, and Blake had wished her well. Meanwhile the distribution deal with Good Earth had come through.

He supposed there were more orthodox ways to run a business—ways people like Doug were taught in business schools. But Blake had always done things in his own fashion, and so far life hadn't treated him too shabbily. Everything was working out, more or less.

"All right, so we'll go to Chicago," he conceded, eager to get Doug out of his office.

Doug's scowl changed into a sulky, anxious expression. "You can work your magic on the Good Earth people, can't you?"

"Doug, the magic I worked isn't the kind of magic a guy should work on a woman who's engaged to marry someone else." Since Doug wasn't gravitating toward the door, Blake stood and circled his desk to escort him out. Actually, it was more of a table than a desk. Blake wasn't a desk type of guy. The lady the company had hired to help with the decor of the offices in the new building had been a bit bemused by him, but she'd found him a really nice, big, sturdy table that, she insisted, "projected authority." More important than authority, as far as he was concerned, was that he could prop his feet up on it without tipping it over.

Actually, his office looked pretty good. The shelves were filled with books and monthly reports; an enlarged and framed photo of the surf pounding against the dunes at the National Seashore north of Orleans hung on the wall, next to a mock poster he'd gotten as a gift from a woman he used to be involved with. It looked like a World War II-era advertisement for bottled cola, except that the clean-cut sailor and his sweet sixteen girlfriend were holding bottles of Blake's Fruit Brews instead. Jenny had given it to him for Christmas. He'd given her something—he couldn't remember what. By February, they were no longer talking to each other. But he really liked the poster.

Doug was stalling, hovering near the door but refusing to leave. He probably feared that Blake wasn't
convinced of the gravity of the situation in Chicago.
That was one of his favorite phrases—"Do you realize
the gravity of the situation?"—and Blake was surprised that he hadn't used it yet this morning.

"Look," Blake said, figuring that if he helped Doug
out a little, Doug might go away. "I recognize the
gravity of the situation. We'll go out to Chicago and
kiss butt, okay?"

Doug had seemed hopeful until those last few
words. "This isn't a joke," he reminded Blake. "We've
finally got the Midwest distribution in place. Now is
not a good time to lose one of our biggest contracts."

"I know, I know. We won't lose them. We'll go and
make everything right." He gave Doug's shoulder a
light nudge, urging him toward the door.

Out in the hall, a couple of secretaries were chatting
near the door to the supply room. Blake would bet
they were thrilled to have a supply room to go to, and
halls wide enough to stand and gossip in. The old
building had been crowded and inhospitable. Blake
hoped everyone would be a lot more comfortable in
Blake's Brew's new home.

"Hey, Martha," one of the secretaries called over
her shoulder. Martha Cooper appeared from around a
bend in the hall, a stack of papers in her hand.

Blake nearly did a double take. Martha looked...
different.

He stared at her from his office doorway, hoping
she wouldn't notice that he was gawking. After a minute, he realized that she didn't look at all different, not
in any definable way. Her hair was the same as it had
been Saturday evening—although a little neater and a

whole lot shinier. Did it always have those reddish
undertones? He'd thought her hair was pretty dark,
but there was definitely a hint of red mixed in with the
brown. Maybe the cheerful lighting in the hallway
was bringing out the highlights.

The hallway lights might also explain why her eyes
seemed brighter. Darker and brighter both. Like
flames—luminous on the perimeter and mysteriously
dark in the middle. Her cheeks looked a little rosier
than usual, too. It had rained all day yesterday, so she
couldn't have been out in the sun. But her face had a
glow to it.

Amazing what a woman could do with a little bit of
makeup, he thought.

Why was Martha Cooper wearing makeup? He
didn't recall ever seeing her in anything more than a
subtle lipstick in all the months she'd worked for him.
And it didn't look as if she had on any of that stuff
women liked to cake onto their eyes, the liner and the
black gunk on their lashes, and the weird colors they
painted onto their eyelids. The only thing unusual
about Martha's eyes was their strange, fiery power.

She looked taller, too. He lowered his gaze, curious
to see if she was wearing high heels instead of her
usual comfortable flat-soled shoes. She had on her regular style of footwear, but her legs, exposed beneath
her skirt, looked mighty nice.

For some incomprehensible reason, he suddenly felt
horny again.

Geez. Martha Cooper? Why on earth would he be
feeling that way about her? The secretaries were
younger, dressed in flirtier clothes. There was nothing
the least bit flirty about Martha. Her skirt was knee-
length, and above it she had on a boring white blouse

and an equally boring blazer. But the blouse was open at her throat, and he glimpsed an oval shadow in the hollow where her collarbones met, and her skin looked like satin.

"So, I'll go ahead and have Helen book the trip to Chicago," Doug yammered into his ear.

"Whatever." Martha had broken from the secretaries after exchanging a few words with them, and resumed her stroll down the hall. She glanced to her left and her gaze met Blake's. To his astonishment, she blushed.

No, she didn't. Martha Cooper was too pragmatic to blush. She was an accountant. Accountants blushed at questionable tax ploys, maybe, but—no, Martha wasn't blushing. It was just the strange lighting in the hallway. Once he got used to it, Martha would look like Martha again.

"Hi," he called to her.

"Hi, Blake. Hi, Doug," she greeted them both. If she *had* blushed, maybe it was because of Doug. If any man in the company seemed like a romantic prospect for Martha, Doug had to be the one, with his expensive suits and his earnest personality.

That must be it. She must have fixed herself up a little nicer that morning because she wanted to impress Doug. Why not? They were both straight-arrow single professionals. They both took life pretty damned seriously. Blake wondered why he'd never made the connection before.

"Maybe we ought to bring Martha to Chicago with us," he murmured once she'd continued down the hall and out of sight.

"Martha?" Doug's eyebrows flickered up and down. "Martha Cooper?"

"I just...I was thinking, maybe if she's there, she can dazzle them with her numbers."

Doug weighed the idea. "I don't know...I don't suppose it would hurt having her there. She does have a way with figures."

Like her own, Blake almost said, then frowned and shook his head, wondering where that thought came from. He'd never before considered Martha as having a way with her figure—or having a figure at all. He'd never really *looked* at her, he realized. He'd depended on her to do her job, and she did it fantastically. When he needed data, she supplied it. When a billing problem lurked, she alerted him to it. When the figures weren't adding up, she figured them out.

But her *figure?*

Well, yeah, she did have nice legs. And her posture seemed proud, displaying her trim hips, her narrow waist and her small, firm breasts. That skirt might not be a hot little mini, but she looked awfully good in it.

Why not? Martha Cooper was a woman. She owned a dog. She lived near the beach. None of this should be making Blake's head spin.

The only reason his head was spinning, he assured himself, was because of his peculiar weekend. He was running on too little sleep. Everything seemed slightly off-kilter today. Once he'd enjoyed a good, solid eight hours of sleep—ideally, preceded by some good, solid sex—the universe would return to normal.

"I'll set it up, then," Doug said. "Chicago, ASAP. And if you want, we'll bring Martha with us."

"Make sure she knows the plan," Blake said. He imagined Martha's eyes growing brighter as Doug informed her she would be traveling with him and Blake to Chicago. He imagined her preening a little, maybe touching her hair, smiling shyly and saying she could arrange her schedule to accompany them. He imagined her adding a little skip to her step because she and Doug would be traveling together, and who knew what could happen while they were away?

He couldn't begin to guess why imagining it caused him a twinge of jealousy.

ONE THING SHE KNEW: whoever had been in her bed during that extra hour early Sunday morning wasn't Blake.

Seeing him standing in his doorway, she'd been struck by his resemblance to the mystery man who had loved her so sublimely during her daylight saving hour. He was exactly as tall, exactly as lean. His hair was exactly the same length, his chest exactly as broad, his shoulders exactly as sturdy.

But he'd stared at her almost as if he'd never even seen her before. That was how significant she was to him. Whoever had visited her bed in the wee hours of the weekend had been a figment of her imagination.

When she'd awakened later that Sunday morning, she'd been positive she'd dreamed the whole erotic incident—even though she'd discovered herself naked, her pajamas strewn on the floor and the pillows misshapen. Pulling herself out of bed, she'd felt aches in muscles she'd forgotten she had. Her thighs were sore, her breasts tender.

Could a dream leave a woman so ravished?

Obviously it could, and she wasn't complaining. To be sure, she would have been inordinately pleased if she could repeat the dream every night. But no visitor materialized in her bedroom at 2:00 a.m. Monday morning, and the digits on her clock radio never vanished. It had been a night like any other.

Determined not to obsess about it, she settled into her chair and surveyed her new office. Her furniture had been arranged in an orderly way.

It was so boring, she thought. She needed some bright prints on the walls, and a plant or two on the windowsill.

She glanced at her watch. Over lunch she would scoot down to the Cape Cod Mall and shop for knickknacks and wall hangings. Given her decision to wear a skirt, and the road puddles left by Sunday's precipitation, she'd driven her car to work instead of biking. A wise move in retrospect, now that she'd resolved to go shopping.

She placed her papers in a file, then swiveled in her chair to summon a budget file from her computer. The light rap on her door frame caused her to swivel back. Dougl Horowitz filled her doorway. "Have you got a minute?" he asked.

She always had a minute for Doug. He was one of the few people in the company hierarchy who actually had an academic grasp of business theory. He tended to fret too much, but she felt he provided a good counterbalance to Blake, who tended to fret too little.

"What's up?" she asked with a smile.

He stepped into her office, looking mildly uneasy. Had he noticed her nervousness when she'd greeted Blake a few minutes ago? Had he observed her blushing? Heaven help her, was he going to comment on it? If he did, she'd crawl under her desk and hide. Or shove him out the door and slam it shut behind him.

"Blake wants you to go to Chicago," he said.

"Chicago?"

"He and I are going. Our Good Earth account has unexpectedly become doubtful. We've got to do some major rescue work. Blake thought you might have something to contribute."

She opened her mouth and closed it. That a potentially huge account in the Midwest was teetering didn't bode well, but what could she possibly contribute to the salvage effort? Budget reports and invoices?

"Why?" she asked.

"I guess he wants you there. Who knows?" Doug flipped his hands palms up as if to say, don't ask me. "Maybe he thinks you can charm the Good Earth people."

Martha laughed out loud. "Charm isn't exactly my strong suit."

"Then maybe he's figuring you'll wow them with your wisdom. You know how Blake is. He gets an idea and he runs with it. He's been right enough times to trust his instincts. His instincts right now are telling him you should come with us to Chicago."

Martha ruminated. "When is this rescue mission supposed to take place?"

"I don't know. I was going to have Helen set it up. We have to contact the Good Earth people and make sure they'll meet with us. The minute I've got some dates I'll let you know."

"Because I have to make arrangements for my dog," she explained.

"You could board the dog for a few days. Blake's Brews will pay for it."

Martha wasn't thrilled with the idea of putting Lucy in a kennel, but she liked the idea of having the company cover the expense. The firm where she used to work in Boston was so huge, she never got to travel for the company. Business trips to visit clients were reserved only for the upper echelon of the accounting department.

But at Blake's Fruit Brews, she was the accounting department, all by herself. If an accountant had to go on a trip for the company, she supposed she'd be the one to go.

She still wasn't sure she had to go on this trip. Her job was to oversee the tax liabilities and monitor the income and outflow of money at Blake's Brews, not to woo dubious buyers. But Blake wanted her along.

As Doug had pointed out, Blake operated on whims a lot of the time, and his whims had led him to success. Maybe he'd hired Martha on a whim. Martha had certainly interviewed for the job and accepted it on a whim. Why not go to Chicago on a whim?

"All right," she said with a shrug. "Keep me posted."

Nodding, Doug pivoted and started toward her door. At the threshold, he paused and turned back. "Is everything okay with you, Martha?" he asked.

She blinked, her brain calculating what he might actually be asking. Doug Horowitz had never indicated anything other than the most casual, collegial interest in her. Over lunch in the old building, when the business staff would usually gather around someone's desk because there was no employee lounge, he might ask her if she was all moved into her house, or if she'd had an employee stock ownership plan with her former company, but she'd never sensed anything more personal than the usual office chitchat in his questions. Being of the female persuasion, she knew more about him than he knew about her, because the ladies' rest room was grapevine central. She knew that he'd had a brief, failed marriage right after college, that he owned a pricy condo abutting a golf course, that he considered *Pulp Fiction* brilliant and that, although no one could prove it, he didn't like dating women who were smarter than he. In sum, it was more than Martha had really wanted to know.

His unexpected solicitousness piqued her curiosity, though. Did he want to know what her favorite movie was? Not *Pulp Fiction*, that was for sure.

"Everything's fine," she said, watching him closely, trying to read his expression. He looked bemused, studying her just as intently. When his silence lasted long enough to bother her, she asked, "Why? Do I look as if something's wrong?"

"No. You look...I don't know. Different." He tilted his head slightly. "As a matter of fact, you look great."

"In other words, I didn't use to look great," she goaded him.

He squirmed and grinned sheepishly. "I didn't say that. It's just...I don't know. There's something different about you. I wish I could put my finger on it."

I look like a woman who got laid, she thought crudely, then amended that: *like a woman who made heavenly love with a stranger for a magical hour over the weekend*. Of course, she hadn't *really* made love, or even gotten laid. Whatever had occurred at two o'clock Sunday morning had occurred only in her imagination.

"I don't know," he said for the third time. "But whatever it is, keep it up. It's obviously good for you."

She clamped her mouth shut to keep from laughing—or wailing. She'd love to have regular visits from her imaginary stud, but he'd been her gift for that one hour, and she wasn't going to see that hour again until a year from now, the next time daylight saving time ended. In the meantime, next spring, when daylight saving time would begin, the hour was going to be stolen from her. What would happen then? Would she be subjected to an hour of torment to compensate for her hour of ecstasy? How could a gift be negated?

"Well." He took a step backward, and another step and grinned again. "I'll have Helen set things up for Chicago," he said, then turned and left her office.

She swiveled back to her computer, but didn't call up a file. Instead, she stared at the swirling screen saver and wondered whether it was obvious to everyone that something had happened to her over the weekend. If Doug had noticed it, had the secretaries in the hall? Had Blake?

Of course he hadn't. Blake never noticed her at all.

4

THE SEAT WAS too small for Blake's long legs. The airport in Barnstable couldn't handle bigger planes, though—and he considered himself lucky he'd been able to book three seats on a direct flight to Chicago, even if those seats were located on a twin-prop puddle jumper instead of a jet.

He was seated by himself in the single-seat row to the left of the aisle; across the way the seats were paired, and he had urged Martha and Doug to sit together. Now he was regretting it. He'd wanted his own seat because he was afraid that every time he moved he would have kicked whoever was sitting next to him, and he'd wanted Martha and Doug together because he thought he sensed some kind of chemistry between them. He wasn't sure why he should think they had possibilities as a couple, let alone why he should care. Matchmaking had never been a hobby of his. Yet they seemed right for each other, two brainy business types, both single, both well educated. Why shouldn't they sit together for the trip to Chicago?

Because seeing them bow their heads together, murmuring and laughing, was bothering the hell out of him.

The drone of the engines drowned out their voices. He supposed it didn't matter what they were saying, anyway. What mattered was that whenever Doug spoke Martha tilted her head slightly, and her hair spilled over her shoulder in a surprisingly feminine way, and her dark eyes glowed. What mattered was that when the flight attendant brought them soft drinks, Doug took Martha's and passed it to her, and his fingers brushed her hand. What mattered was that Blake was sitting all by himself, watching them and feeling increasingly disgruntled.

When the flight attendant turned from them to offer him a drink, he requested a beer. She pulled a can of domestic from her cart and handed it to him, along with a bag of peanuts and a plastic smile. He nodded and turned away, refusing to pop open the can until she'd moved farther down the aisle. He sipped his beer directly from the can, then scowled at its icy blandness. Flights ought to carry Blake's Fruit Brews on their beverage carts, he thought—much tastier than soda or watery canned juices. He'd like to discuss the idea with his business staff across the aisle. But they were busy sipping ginger ale and gazing into each other's eyes.

Why had he decided to bring Martha Cooper on this trip?

There was something about her. Something that had been niggling at him ever since that night he'd driven her home from the new headquarters. Or maybe what was niggling at him had nothing to do with her at all.

What he needed to do was shake off whatever was bugging him and concentrate on the task at hand: securing the Good Earth account. He shouldn't be squandering his gray matter trying to guess what Doug was whispering to Martha and what she was laughing about, or trying to figure out why he hadn't managed to get a solid night's sleep since that Saturday night a couple of weeks ago.

He'd probably feel better if he and Tracy got together in Chicago. They'd had a good thing last spring—not a lasting thing, obviously, but they'd parted as friends, and seeing her would cheer him up. Tracy was the exact opposite of Martha, the *anti*-Martha. A while spent in her company would help him to put Martha into perspective.

As if he needed perspective when it came to Martha. She was his accountant. End of story.

She was laughing again. Despite the incessant growl of the plane's engines, he could hear her laughter. Or maybe he was imagining it, supplying his own soundtrack to the sight of her tossing her head back and grinning at something Doug had said. Cripes. In all the months she'd worked for Blake, he hadn't seen her laugh as much as she was laughing on this one flight.

She and Doug had both brought their laptops with them. Why didn't they pull out their equipment and get to work? Or play solitaire. Anything but lean toward each other and indulge in witty exchanges, separated from Blake by an aisle that seemed as broad and deep as the Grand Canyon.

Think about Tracy, he reminded himself. *Think about Good Earth. Plot your strategy.*

If all went well, he wouldn't have to drag Tracy into it. She'd offered him access to Good Earth, but she'd never been a part of the actual negotiations. He was grateful to her for what she'd done, and in gratitude he ought to avoid complicating her life, now that she was engaged to be married. But he'd be damned if he was going to let the Good Earth account slip through his fingers. Doug might be the business whiz, but Blake knew a thing or two about how to build a company and make it profitable. He'd spent the past ten years doing just that.

The flight attendant announced that they were beginning their final approach to Midway Airport. Blake's legs twitched in anticipation of being liberated from the confines of his seat. Through the window he could see the sprawl of Chicago, roofs and cars and gray threads of road. In a matter of minutes they would be on the ground, and Doug and Martha would have to stop whispering and giggling and remember who was the boss.

And the boss would have to get rid of his stupid-ass attitude. He'd included Martha on this trip for Doug's sake. He ought to be pleased they were getting along so well.

The plane touched the tarmac with a thud and a thump. He watched the propellers slow from a circular blur to individual blades as the plane taxied toward a terminal. The plane was too small to pull into a gate, and instead a staircase was wheeled over to the plane. Turning from the window, Blake watched as Doug and Martha stood, hoisted their untouched laptops from under the seats in front of them and edged out into the aisle, Doug politely allowing Martha to precede him. Blake fell into step behind Doug. As soon as Martha reached the open doorway, the sun struck her hair, awakening all the red highlights in it.

Her hair was brown. He told himself this as he followed Doug down the steps to the tarmac. Martha Cooper had mousy brown hair. The chestnut streaks he'd recently noticed in it must have come courtesy of Lady Clairol.

Martha had never struck him as vain enough to color her hair. But maybe she was outrageously vain, and he had simply failed to notice. Or maybe it was that the entire world had seemed slightly askew to Blake ever since that weird night in October, when he'd gained an hour and lost his equilibrium.

An airline employee on the ground unloaded their bags for them. Martha and Doug both had rectangular black suitcases on wheels. Blake had a bright orange duffel. He wouldn't have traded his distinctive bag for their boring dime-a-dozen suitcases, but his having a different bag irked him.

What was his problem? Everything was ticking him off.

"I love those propellor planes," Martha said as she slid the handle out of her suitcase. "I always feel like Amelia Earhart when I'm on them."

Amelia Earhart? Blake would have never guessed Martha's role model would be a daring aviatrix.

He hoisted the strap of his duffel over his shoulder and stalked toward the terminal, glancing behind him to make sure Doug and Martha were with him. They were just a couple of paces back, dragging their twin black suitcases behind them like well-trained pets. Entering the terminal, he followed the signs to ground transportation. He heard the wheels of their suitcases squeaking in harmony as they trailed him down the long corridor to the exit.

A string of cabs waited at the curb, and he snagged the first empty one in the line. If he'd rented a car, either Martha or Doug would have felt obligated to sit in the front seat with him. But in a cab, he wound up in the front seat with the driver, while the two of them climbed into the back. It made sense—the back seat offered less room, and he was the largest of the three. But still...

He felt isolated. No wonder he didn't usually engage in matchmaking. It was a lonesome pursuit for the matchmaker.

"What does our schedule for tomorrow look like?" Doug asked, once Blake had given the driver the name of the downtown hotel where Helen had reserved rooms for them.

Blake twisted to gaze into the back seat. They both looked fresher than he felt after the two-hour flight. Martha still had a dewy radiance about her, a hint of color in her cheeks, an uptick at the corners of her mouth, as if she were close to exploding into a blinding grin. In his eyeglasses, with his hair impeccably combed, Doug looked like a Ralph Lauren model, rich and privileged. Blake—the most powerful person in the car—believed in traveling in comfort, which meant faded jeans, a flannel shirt over a T-shirt, and his battered leather jacket. The irony was that Doug, in his crisp khakis, monogrammed shirt and wool blazer, looked more comfortable than Blake was feeling.

Martha didn't look comfortable or uncomfortable. She just looked nice. Nicer than Blake was used to, when it came to her. He'd been studying her lately, whenever he had the chance, and he was reasonably sure she hadn't resorted to wearing makeup. The pink in her cheeks was apparently her natural complexion, and her eyelashes were dense and dark without mascara. He'd observed her drinking coffee in the lounge back at work, and she never left a lipstick stain on her cup, so he had to conclude her lips were naturally that musky pink color.

She was miles away from being a knockout. She wouldn't turn heads in public. Except...except every time Blake was near her, he found himself wanting to stare. Not because of her riveting beauty, but because he was still trying to figure out what it was about her that had changed.

"We've got a nine-thirty meeting with Bruno Thompson," he remembered to answer Doug.

"Bruno is the CEO of the Good Earth health food store chain," Doug reminded Martha.

"Hopefully, we'll get back on track with them," Blake said. "I thought we could work up a strategy over dinner tonight. Is that okay with you?" He eyed Martha, aware that in her own way, she must feel as out of the loop as he did. She might have spent the entire flight making chitchat with Doug, but she'd never met with a buyer before, never rescued a teetering deal, never worked on any kind of business strategy. She'd been employed by Blake's Brews long enough to have some idea of the way he did things, but the mission of this particular trip was new to her.

He didn't realize he was holding his breath until she nodded that it was okay with her. The air rushed out of his lungs, and he felt like a jerk. "Feel free to contribute tonight," he added, hoping he wasn't coming across as weird as he felt. "I mean it. Any ideas, whatever."

She smiled hesitantly. "If I think of anything, I'll speak up."

"Good." He twisted to face forward and his respiration returned to normal. He had a bunch of questions for her: how her dog was, whether she was still biking now that the temperature was dropping with the approach of winter, whether she had plans for Thanksgiving. Whether part of her enjoyment of the flight had been because Doug was such good company. Whether she'd be at all receptive if Doug made a pass at her.

He risked another quick glimpse into the back seat. Doug was watching Martha, who was smoothing her beige trench coat beneath her seat belt. That was the Martha Cooper he knew—not a daredevil who pretended to be Amelia Earhart on a prop plane, but a number cruncher who buckled her seat belt in a cab. As the towering skyscrapers of Chicago enveloped them, Blake felt just a little less unsettled by the woman in the cab, a woman who had always been a mystery but had lately become a mystery he felt compelled to solve.

TALKING WITH DOUG was so easy. Talking with Blake would never be easy.

Probably because he still had a way of making her feel like a gawky sophomore, breathless in the presence of the best-looking boy in the entire high school.

What on earth did he expect her to contribute to their strategy for approaching this Bruno person? Martha still wasn't sure why she'd been included in the trip. All she knew was that the Winstons, who lived across the street, had agreed to dog-sit for Lucy so Martha wouldn't have to board her in a kennel, and therefore, at some point before Martha returned to Hyannis, she wanted to buy them a thank-you present. A Chicago souvenir of some sort, perhaps, or a bottle of brandy.

She worried about Lucy spending the next few days

with the Winstons. They were lovely people, but Lucy could be a handful when she wanted—and most of the time, she wanted. Martha had left instructions, a sack of dry dog food, two jars of ready-to-serve gravy, a box of puppy treats, two pounds of chopped chuck, a loaf of fresh rye bread—Lucy liked bread with her meals—and the yellow ball that honked when Lucy chomped her teeth into it. She would be fine. She probably wouldn't even miss Martha. In fact, the Winstons would probably fall in love with Lucy and not miss Martha, either. They'd wish she stayed in Chicago forever, so they could keep Lucy for themselves. When Martha got home, Lucy would probably sniff her shoes and run back across the street, whimpering for the Winstons to protect her from her former mistress.

She shouldn't have come on this trip. She wouldn't have come, except that her boss had asked her to come. As a savvy professional, she knew one was wise not to say no to one's boss.

Like hell. She would have gone anywhere if Blake had asked her. Even if he wasn't her boss. Even if it wasn't a professionally savvy thing to do.

Throughout the flight, she'd been keenly aware of him across the aisle, leafing through a binder of papers and sipping his beer. She'd felt a little guilty chatting with Doug instead of working, although she had no pressing work to review on the trip. And Doug, who was as much the brains of Blake's Brews as Blake was the heart of it, hadn't seemed interested in turning on his laptop during the trip. Instead, he'd talked with her, describing the glories of Cape Cod in the winter—the emptiness, the tranquillity of the beaches, the joy of being able to get a tee time at the golf course without making reservations weeks in advance. "Isn't there snow on the golf course?" she'd asked, and he'd explained to her that the Cape got significantly less snow than the rest of Massachusetts.

"If you love golf the way I do," he'd added, "you'd gladly pull on your Thinsulate boots and trudge through the snow to play a round. All you need is a caddie to locate the holes and clear the snow out of them."

Doug was funnier than she'd realized. He was more intense than Blake when it came to business matters, but on the plane he'd been friendly and easygoing, a pleasure to talk to.

Blake was friendly and easygoing, too, she reminded herself as the cab slowed to a crawl in the late afternoon traffic of downtown Chicago. The only reason he wasn't a pleasure to talk to was that his heart-stopping blue eyes always left her feeling embarrassingly tongue-tied when she was around him.

The cab pulled up under the awning of a hotel and stopped. As Blake paid the driver, she automatically said, "Get a receipt," then cringed. She might as well wear a neon sign flashing Accountant across her chest.

Blake dutifully got a receipt from the driver and passed it to Martha, his mouth curved in the sort of smile an obedient pupil might give his teacher. Martha wasn't sure whether she'd prefer for him to view her as an accountant or as a prissy schoolmarm. She told herself that how he viewed her was irrelevant, as long as he was satisfied with her performance on the job. That was the only thing that existed between them, after all.

He led the way across the marble-floored lobby to the registration desk. In his defiantly casual attire, with his bright-orange bag slung over his shoulder, he looked like an explorer about to trek into the sunset. And she and Doug looked like two corporate drudges chasing after him, dressed in their office uniforms and dragging their suitcases behind them.

"I'm figuring we should get settled in our rooms," Blake suggested as he handed his credit card to the clerk behind the desk, "and then we can meet for dinner."

"And make plans for tomorrow," Doug added, as if he didn't trust Blake to remember why they'd come to Chicago.

"Yeah." Blake's gaze circled the vaulted lobby. She scanned it, too: the artfully arranged potted plants, the escalators gliding smoothly to a mezzanine level, the boutiques and convenience shops and the deep leather chairs arranged in conversation pits across the vast expanse of the hotel. People swarmed through the lobby, most of them in business attire like Doug and herself. No one else looked like Blake—no one as handsome, no one as nonchalantly dressed, no one exuding even half as much jaunty charisma. The clerk finished with his credit card, and he extended it to Martha. "You want to take care of this, too?" he asked.

She felt the invisible neon Accountant sign flash across her chest again. When Blake looked at her, he saw a sawdust-dry drudge. She couldn't blame him. She wouldn't be surprised if people who didn't even know her saw a drudge when they looked at her. The only man who'd ever looked at her as if she were not a drab accountant but a passionate woman had been her mysterious visitor that one night...a night she really should avoid thinking about when Blake was around, because whenever she thought about it, she felt her cheeks and other parts of her body grow uncomfortably warm.

"What's the best restaurant in this hotel?" Blake asked the clerk, pocketing his credit card when Martha didn't take it.

The clerk named several eateries at the hotel. "La Fleur is the most elegant," she told him, scrutinizing his casual clothes. "Jackets are required."

"Have you got a place with good food and no jackets?" Blake asked.

The clerk smiled helpfully. Martha wondered whether she was taken with his casual charm. "The Oakwood Room is a little less formal, and the food is excellent."

"Okay." Blake turned to Doug and Martha. "The Oakwood Room, seven o'clock." He handed Doug a packet containing his key, then handed a packet to Martha. His fingertips brushed hers, and the contact jolted her, making her skin tingle the way it had when the mystery man had touched her in her dreams, when daylight saving time was slipping away.

Forget about that night, she ordered herself. *Forget it ever happened.* Forgetting would be a whole lot easier if her mystery man hadn't so strongly resembled the tall, blond hunk standing just inches from her.

The three of them shared an elevator up to the ninth floor, then located their rooms, all in a row, Doug in the middle. Martha would have been surprised if Blake had taken a nicer room for himself, one of the corner suites or something on the concierge level. The top echelon of management at her old firm in Boston would have pulled rank in hotel accommodations—but they'd been obsessed by hierarchies. Blake was the least hierarchical of any executive she'd ever known, even if he had chosen to sit apart from Doug and Martha on the flight. Martha had thought he would want to sit with Doug so they could discuss their plans for restoring Good Earth's contract with them—but she'd gotten the sense that he hadn't sat alone because he didn't want to socialize with his employees. It was more as if he'd wanted to give his employees a chance to socialize without him.

Her room was attractive, the bed broad and firm, the furniture walnut, the windows covered with a translucent drape that let the lights of the city through, small spots of brightness like stars swimming across the fabric. She unpacked, set up her laptop, and took a quick shower.

By five minutes to seven she was dressed in slacks and a textured sweater, her hair blow-dried and her mind fresher than it had been when she'd stepped off the plane an hour ago. She inspected her reflection in the full-length mirror on the bathroom door and decided she looked about fifty on a scale of a hundred, with a three-point margin of error.

Even lacking a neon sign, she looked like what she was. Not an accountant, necessarily, but a slim and healthy but in no way striking-looking woman.

She'd made her peace with her appearance a long time ago. It was only the existence of Blake Robey—the knowledge that he was just two doors away, in a room that was in all likelihood identical to hers, featuring the same broad, inviting bed and the same romantic view of the city's winking lights—that made her so acutely self-conscious.

Sighing, she turned from the mirror, grabbed her purse, her room key and—because she was who she was—her notepad and a pen. As she left the room, she double-checked to make sure the door locked behind her.

Doug and Blake were already in the restaurant when she arrived. She could see them from the doorway, seated at a semicircular banquette, sipping drinks and chuckling about something. Spotting her as she approached their table, they both stood and smiled in welcome. Doug was dressed in typical preppie splendor—crisp oxford shirt and dark slacks—and Blake was dressed in typical beach bum indifference—an open denim shirt over a T-shirt, and jeans.

They seemed like good friends, despite their contrasting styles. For the zillionth time, she wondered why she was here. Surely they could handle Bruno Thompson and his health food empire just fine without her.

Doug slid out from behind the table so she could sit between them. She eyed their drinks—a beer for Blake and something more sophisticated, involving amber fluid and ice cubes, for Doug. A waiter appeared and she asked for a glass of Chablis. As the token woman at the table, she thought that seemed like an appropriate drink.

"I was just telling Blake," Doug said, "that I thought you needed to be brought up to speed."

"About what we're doing tomorrow?" Martha nodded. "I sure do."

"Actually, about the way Blake does business in general. It's not the same way normal people do business."

"I'm normal," Blake protested.

"The CEO of the Good Earth chain has a daughter named Tracy," Doug explained. "Blake met her somewhere—where was it, Blake? Aruba?"

"Jamaica," Blake corrected him.

"Jamaica. Anyway, it was thanks to their friendship that we gained entry to Good Earth. That friendship is no longer what it used to be, however."

The waiter arrived with Martha's wine and a stack of menus. She skimmed one, ordering the first palatable entree she saw just to speed the process along. She was fascinated by Doug's tale and wanted to hear more about this "friendship" between Blake and Tracy that was no longer what it used to be.

The men took their time, debating the relative merits of T-bones versus sirloins before Doug wound up ordering prime rib and Blake selected a pasta-and-seafood dish. "Sirloins are always more tender," Doug insisted even as the waiter distributed water and rolls and tiny pots of butter around the table.

"Jamaica," Martha prompted him.

"Right. Jamaica. They were friends," Doug said.

"And now they're—what? Enemies?" She risked a glimpse at Blake, whose smile looked forced as Doug reviewed his social life.

"Not enemies," he clarified. "Still friends. The thing is, Tracy is engaged to be married."

"Ah. I see." What Martha saw was that "friends" was a euphemism for what Blake and Tracy had been to each other in Jamaica.

"What this means is, we've lost our leverage with Tracy's father, who makes the ultimate decisions about what he stocks in his stores," Doug explained.

Martha might have accepted this tale with a worldly shrug. But she wasn't worldly, and she tended to view business ethics in a rather stringent way. "You slept with this woman to get your product in her father's stores?" she asked, hoping she'd misunderstood. She would hate to be working for someone who used sex to improve his product distribution.

Blake looked affronted. "Of course not. I didn't even know who her father was when we met. We hit it off, we had a good time, and the thing with her father came out much later, after I told her about Blake's Brews. It was her idea to talk to her father about our stuff."

"Last spring," Doug continued, "we shipped an assortment of juices, and Bruno loved the product. He thought it would sell well in his stores, given that they feature organic, health-oriented foods and drinks. It looked like a great match, a fantastic way to expand our market. So Bruno's decision to back off all of a sudden has real ramifications. He hasn't been clear about why he's changing direction. We're here to make nice with him, woo him back, remind him of what a perfect fit Blake's Brews and Good Earth are."

Martha listened, nodded, eyed Blake furtively and decided she was glad he looked less than serene as Doug filled her in on the history of their relationship with Good Earth. He *should* be uncomfortable, she thought indignantly. Regardless of the order in which things happened in Jamaica, he ought to be ashamed that he'd gotten his foot in Good Earth's door by getting his body into Bruno Thompson's daughter's bed.

One thing didn't make sense, though: "I still don't understand why I'm here."

"I thought you could help," Blake said, his gaze shuttling between her and Doug.

"How can I help? I'm an accountant." Just in case he couldn't see the invisible neon sign.

"You're smart," Blake said vaguely. "You'll think of something."

Not likely. All she could think of was that someone ought to have taught Blake the proper way to conduct business before he'd founded his own company.

Granted, the company was successful, it was practically booming, and Blake was clearly doing a lot of things right. But this? Martha couldn't recall any courses in her entire college curriculum that offered instruction in how to seduce a woman so her father would stock your products.

Blake hadn't gone to business school; what he knew he'd learned from experience, from trial and error and the dictates of his intuition. Whatever he'd experienced in Jamaica, whatever mistakes he might have made and intuitions he might have followed, Bruno Thompson hadn't greeted him at the airport with a shotgun. Blake had worked his way into the man's good graces once. As appalled as Martha was by how he'd accomplished that, she was admittedly curious to see if he could accomplish it again, this time without the assistance of Bruno's daughter.

Martha knew just how good Blake's Fruit Brews were. She didn't know how good Blake was. Tomorrow she'd find out.

5

BLAKE WAITED for Martha near the entry to the Acorn Café at seven-thirty the following morning. They'd agreed to meet there for breakfast before heading out to Good Earth's headquarters for their nine-thirty meeting. He spotted her emerging from the elevator alcove, dressed in a burgundy suit, a white blouse, black pumps on her feet, her trench coat draped over one arm and her laptop case clutched in the other hand. His gaze remained on her as she crossed the lobby.

She really had great legs.

He swore under his breath. Something was seriously wrong with him, and his awareness of Martha Cooper's legs was an obvious symptom. Something had started being wrong that night daylight saving time ended, and it had continued being wrong ever since. And now it was even more wrong, because he had terrible news to share with her and all he could think of was the appealing curves of her calves, the delicate ovals of her kneecaps and the slenderness of her ankles emphasized by the dark tint of her stockings.

Terrible news. Potentially tragic news. And he was feeling like a sex-starved idiot, wondering what his company's accountant would look like in a garter belt. And nothing else.

She closed the distance between them and smiled blandly. "Where's Doug?" she asked.

"I've got terrible news," he warned her, then took her elbow and guided her into the café. She shot him an alarmed look but he didn't elaborate, speaking only to tell the hostess they needed a table for two and coffee right away. Once they were seated, facing each other, he saw that she was pale, her eyes wide with worry.

"What terrible news?"

"Doug had to leave." He paused while a waitress delivered two heavy mugs of steaming coffee and a pitcher of cream to the table. Once she was gone, he studied Martha across the table. It didn't take sunshine to bring out the reddish highlights in her hair, he realized. The artificial light of the café was doing the trick just as well.

"Leave?" she asked, jerking his attention back to the subject at hand.

"His father had a heart attack last night. He's at Beth-Israel Hospital, and the doctors have him stabilized. But Doug felt he needed to be with his mother. So he flew back to Boston."

"Of course." She lowered her eyes to her mug, then took a sip and shook her head. "That's awful. I feel so bad for him."

"I think he's going to be okay. Doug's father, I mean." Blake observed her closely, trying not to be obvious. Was she heartbroken that Doug was gone? Had she been hoping something might develop between them on this trip? Or was her dismal expression just a natural response to sad news?

And why, if Blake was so sure something might be developing between her and Doug, was he still thinking about her legs? He had to be insane. Yet it took all his willpower not to ask her if by some strange quirk she was a garter-belt woman instead of a panty hose woman.

To distract himself, he picked up one menu and passed the other to her. Skimming the beverage listings, he contemplated the possibility of getting Blake's Fruit Juices into the hotel-restaurant loop. Why should hotel eateries serve just orange, tomato, prune and cranberry juice when they could serve his blended fruit drinks? Blake's Brews were just as healthy—all natural, no sugar added—but a hell of a lot tastier than prune juice.

Geez. What was he turning into? A corporate lecher. A guy with a two-track mind, one of those tracks business and the other garter belts. Perhaps this was a sign that he was growing up. Not long ago, he had only a one-track mind, and that track hadn't been business.

Still, it was weird that the garter-belt track seemed to be leading to the Martha Cooper station. She was so perfect for Doug, which by definition should mark her as perfectly wrong for Blake. Doug's type couldn't possibly be *his* type. The truth was, until recently, he hadn't even thought of Martha as anyone's type at all.

The waitress returned to refill their mugs and take their orders—fresh fruit and waffles for him, a toasted bagel for her. Once they were alone again, Martha asked, "When did Doug leave?"

"Five this morning. It was the first flight he could get out on. His mother called around midnight last night, and then he called me and we got in touch with the airline. They make allowances for medical emergencies."

She nodded. "I hope he'll phone and let us know if everything's okay."

"Yeah, I told him to give us a buzz if he had a free minute. I don't know when he'll have a free minute, though."

"It's scary." She sipped her coffee and ruminated. "I hate thinking about my parents getting older. They're both in excellent health. I want them to stay that way."

"Mine, too." The muscles along his spine relaxed and he leaned back in his chair. It occurred to him that his mind had more than two tracks, after all. The third track had been traveling back to Boston in Doug's wake, preoccupied with thoughts about parents and health and the frailties of age. He never used to think about those things—his parents were strong and healthy. But they were also in their fifties, and after that they would be in their sixties, and then their seventies. And anyway, a person couldn't help worrying about the people he loved. "My father had knee surgery a couple of years ago, that arthroscopic procedure. He banged up his knee years ago while skiing, and it degenerated over time, so they had to go in and tidy up the joint, literally." She flickered a faint smile at his pun. He smiled back, then grew serious again. "It wasn't a big thing, but—" he shrugged "—it's kind of weird to see your old man on crutches, you know?"

"We like to think our parents will always be there for us, at a hundred-percent strength," she said.

"Yeah. Even people who don't get along with their parents—I think it would still be a shock to see your dad in a hospital bed, looking weak and pale."

"It's because they're all that stand between us and our own mortality," Martha suggested. "When they get sick or hurt, we feel unprotected. Our parents gave us life and took care of us. They were our first defense against the world. Losing them would make us feel defenseless."

The waitress arrived with their breakfast. As she arranged the plates on the table, Blake took a moment to consider the fact that he and Martha had just had the most personal discussion of their acquaintance. In fact, it might be the most personal discussion he'd ever had with anyone from the company. He didn't talk about his family much. They were terrific, he loved them, and none of it was anybody's business. He didn't keep photos of his sister's kids on his desk. He didn't have his mother dropping in for lunch on her way to the mall. It wasn't as if he had anything to hide. He just wasn't into sharing all that personal stuff, not when it came to the people he worked with or the women he dated.

But the concerns were inside him, and the love. It had felt good to discuss his parents and share his feelings with Martha. She was easier to talk to than he would have guessed.

He picked up his fork and knife, sliced a wedge of waffle, then realized she was staring at him, her knife idle in one hand and a naked bagel half cradled in the other. "Maybe we ought to postpone the meeting with the Good Earth people until Doug can be there," she said.

"Nah. We came to Chicago. We may as well go ahead and talk to them. We can handle it without Doug."

"Maybe you can." She tore her eyes from him and smeared a dab of cream cheese onto the bagel. "I don't even belong here."

"Yes, you do," he said quickly. If she wasn't with him, he'd definitely cancel the meeting. But even though she wasn't an expert in marketing like Doug, he needed her with him. Just her presence counted for a lot. Blake alone against Bruno Thompson and his board would be a mismatch. With two people on their side, they wouldn't seem quite so badly outnumbered.

"All I know about this deal is what you told me yesterday," she reminded him. "You had an affair with a stranger in Jamaica and wound up doing business with her father. And now her father has had second thoughts. What am I supposed to do?"

"You took business courses in college, right?"

"Not contracts and negotiations."

"You still know more about that stuff than me."

"But you have an instinct for it," she argued. "I don't."

He wanted to ask her what she had an instinct for. Something more than adding columns of numbers, he knew, something more than understanding the irrational tangles of the tax code and the balance between gains and losses, assets and debits. He'd bet she had instincts for other things, human things, things like taking care of her dog and worrying about her parents and getting Blake to talk about subjects he never talked about.

"Just spout numbers," he suggested. "Sound authoritative. I'll charm them. You can back me up."

"As long as I don't have to charm them," she muttered, although a smile teased her lips. "If you were counting on me for charm, we'd be in a lot of trouble."

"You can be charming," he said, not sure whether he meant she *was* charming or she *could* be if she wanted to. Martha had never attempted to charm him—at least not that he'd ever noticed—yet she'd charmed him without trying this morning. And other times, too, he was sure. He just couldn't pinpoint when.

As they ate, Blake told her a little more about Bruno Thompson. "He's kind of weird," he said. "A hard-nosed businessman, but also a health-food fanatic. Anyone who thinks running a successful business is a red-meat sport should meet him. You'd be surprised how cutthroat a tofu eater can be."

"Is he a vegetarian?"

"No, but he actually likes tofu. He eats all that stuff—soy paste and bean sprouts and veggieburgers. And roast beef and ham. He doesn't like to get pinned down."

"Maybe the best strategy is to emphasize how good Blake's Fruit Brews taste and stay away from how healthy the product is. It sounds as if he's more interested in how foods taste than in whether they're low in cholesterol."

"Yeah." Blake had read her right: she had good instincts. "We'll emphasize the flavor. The variety. The demographics of his clientele." He chuckled. "Wow. When I use words like that, I almost sound like Doug."

"Good. When you're done charming them, you can sound authoritative. I'll just sit in the back of the room and take notes."

"If I'm going to have to do the authoritative bit," Blake warned, "you're going to have to do the charm. I'm not doing both." And he would love to see Martha Cooper do charm. Just for the hell of it. Just to see how charming she could be if she put her mind to it.

GOOD EARTH'S headquarters occupied several floors of an intimidating high-rise on Michigan Avenue. Definitely a meat eater's address, not a tofu eater's, Martha thought wryly.

She'd spent the cab drive mentally preparing herself for the meeting, shoving away the three huge distractions that threatened her: first, her concern about Doug and his father; second, her honest acknowledgment that she was not the right person for this mission; and third, her unrelenting awareness of Blake. He had gone to some effort to make himself presentable that morning: pleated slacks of pale-gray flannel, a dress shirt, a navy wool blazer and leather loafers. No tie, but for Blake it was a pretty formal outfit—and seeing him in it proved to Martha that he looked as formidably handsome dressed up as he did dressed down.

Yesterday's cab ride had been easier on her nervous system, because he'd ridden in the front seat. This morning found them side by side on the back seat. A wedge of space separated them, but she was viscerally conscious of every inch of that space, every cubic centimeter of air between them. She was conscious of the scent of his aftershave, the glint of his pale hair in the morning sun, the angle of his jaw, the knife-edge sharpness of his nose in profile. She was conscious of his blunt fingers as he rested hands on his knees, his broad shoulders filling his jacket, the length of his legs folded to fit into the narrow space, his knees brushing against the back of the front seat.

Bottom lines were her specialty, and at the moment the bottom line was that Blake was a marvel of masculine charisma. It didn't matter if she broke him down into fingers and jawline, blue eyes and spicy fragrance. She could analyze each aspect of him and conclude that it was appealing, but the sum was far greater than all those appealing parts, and the lack of mathematical logic in her Blake Robey computation irked her sensibilities.

They rode the elevator up to a high floor and emerged into a spacious lobby decorated with ugly tables and chairs and abstract prints on the walls. "Good Earth rents a lot of square footage in this building," Blake warned her, taking her elbow and ushering her through a glass doubledoor to the receptionist's desk. "They're not as big as the big supermarket chains, but for a health food outlet, they're pretty impressive."

"I'm impressed," Martha assured him. At her old firm in Boston, she worked on impressive accounts, too—but she was low on the totem pole and didn't have to face company presidents in skyscraper suites. She squared her shoulders and gripped her laptop case, determined not to let the meat-eating, tofu-loving mogul intimidate her.

"Blake Robey," Blake identified himself to the receptionist, then gave her one of his heart-stopping smiles. "And this is Martha Cooper. We've got a nine-thirty appointment with Bruno Thompson."

"I'll let him know you're here," the receptionist said, giving Blake an embarrassingly starry-eyed gaze before she lifted her receiver and tapped a few buttons on her console. "Mr. Robey is here to see Mr. Thompson," she recited, her face tilted up and her voice breathy as she continued to gaze at him, utterly transfixed. She listened for a moment, then nodded and hung up. "Please follow me," she beckoned. Martha hoped the poor young woman wouldn't swoon en route to Thompson's office.

She led them down a hallway to a private elevator, every now and then glancing over her shoulder as if to make sure Blake hadn't abandoned her. Martha might have been invisible for all the attention the receptionist paid her.

The elevator door glided open and she led them inside. "The conference room is upstairs," she said, pushing a button. Given the vast size of Good Earth's corporate headquarters, Martha imagined that the conference room would be enormous. She and Blake would sit at one end of a fifteen-foot-long table, and Thompson and an army of vice presidents would sit at the other. Blake's charm could go pretty far, but her faked authoritativeness was bound to evaporate in such an environment.

They stepped out of the elevator on an upper floor. The corridor was decorated in the rich, dark hues of a staid Boston law firm—forest-green carpeting, mahogany-paneled walls, flowers in vases. Their footsteps muffled by the plush carpet, they followed the receptionist down a hall and into a room which, to Martha's great relief, was actually quite small. The table had only eight chairs around it, and the curtains were drawn back to display a view of the city below.

"Wait right here," the receptionist said, her eyes zeroing in on Blake. "Can I get you anything?"

"Have you got any Blake's Fruit Brews?" Blake asked, completely straight-faced.

She blinked. "I'm sorry, I've never heard of that. What is it?"

He shot Martha a look that seemed to say, *What a twit!* "Nothing for me, then, thanks. Martha, you want anything?"

She was touched that he thought to mention her af-

ter the receptionist had done such a thorough job of ignoring her. "No, thanks," she said, giving the young
woman a sweet smile.

The receptionist backed out of the room, then pivoted and vanished down the hall. Martha and Blake
stood in silence for a minute, surveying their surroundings. "Where do you think we should sit?" Martha asked.

Blake scowled. "On the windowsill. These chairs
look so stiff. If you sat in one, they might just strap
your wrists, shave your head and buzz fifty-thousand
volts through you."

She laughed. She shouldn't have—she was supposed to be mentally preparing herself to act authoritative—but he was right. The chairs had straight, high
backs and rigid seats. Their appearance did have a
certain punitive quality.

"What do they teach you in business school?" he
asked her. "Which seat gives you the most testosterone?"

"I don't want a seat that will give me testosterone,"
she said dryly.

"You know what I mean. Power. Dominance. Su-
premacy."

"Who says that's synonymous with testosterone?"

Footsteps and voices in the hall kept him from answering her. Within a minute, the doorway filled with
a tall, husky man of middle age, with an unlined face
and silver hair pulled back into a neat ponytail. His
suit had the odd fit of something put together by a
fashion designer trying to make a statement. Martha
would bet he'd paid a fortune for it.

He presented Blake with his right hand and a toothy

smile. "Blake!" he boomed, pumping Blake's hand and slapping his back. "Good to see you!"

"Bruno," Blake greeted him, his smile subtler and cannier. "Good seeing you, too. This is Martha Cooper," he introduced her.

"Martha!" Bruno bellowed, crushing her fingers in a bruising handshake.

She found it ironic that a health food magnate would be so...*beefy.* "How do you do?" she said politely.

"And these are my veeps," Bruno said, gesturing toward the woman and two men who'd accompanied him into the room. If Martha were a vice president of anything, she wouldn't want to be introduced as a "veep." Their names blurred past her, and then they took their seats around the table, Martha and Blake on one side, two of the Good Earth executives across from them, the third and Bruno at the ends. Martha didn't think hers was the testosterone seat. Sitting in it, she felt no sudden rush of power, and her chin didn't sprout hair.

The discussion began. Bruno gave Martha and Blake an unnecessary lecture on the pressures of inventory management and the challenges of product selection. He pointed out the need to stock his stores with products he knew he could sell, products for which his customers had demonstrated a preference. He had a small profit margin, he explained, although Martha was skeptical about that, and he couldn't waste shelf space on high-risk new products.

"The thing is, you love Blake's Fruit Brews," Blake reminded him, his tone so languid he sounded on the verge of falling asleep. "You've drunk them yourself. You said you loved them."

"I'm not questioning the quality of your product," Bruno allowed. "It's a fine drink—"

"And healthy, too," Blake added. "No chemicals, no sweeteners, nothing but fruit juices blended together. It's good stuff."

"No argument, Blake. It's good stuff. Isn't it good stuff?" Bruno asked his underlings, who obediently nodded.

"It's the kind of beverage that would go over big with your customers," Blake insisted. Martha admired him in silence. He didn't sound aggressive or desperate. Rather, his attitude was almost altruistic, as if he were trying to save Bruno from making a critical mistake.

"It might," Bruno conceded, shooting Blake another orthodontist-dream smile. "The thing is, we carry other fruit juices in the chain now. And they're produced—well, not locally, but certainly closer to home. Importing Blake's fruit juices from Cape Cod doesn't seem practical at this time."

"As part of our expansion," Blake told him, "we'll be opening a Midwestern distributorship. There's nothing long distance about it."

"You aren't opening the distributorship until after you've locked into a deal with us, though," Bruno pointed out. "The distributorship would come after we made our commitment."

"But it would be there." Blake shrugged, as if he considered Bruno's argument irrelevant. "You'd get your stock fresh and on time. That's all that matters."

Martha sat quietly, rubbing the toe of her shoe against the canvas of her laptop case. She felt useless, except that Blake had insisted her presence alone would be a valuable contribution. It didn't seem enough to her, but what could she say? She was an accountant. She could explain what a contract with Good Earth would do to the company's profitability, but that wasn't going to win any arguments with Bruno Thompson.

"So, how's Tracy doing?" Blake asked abruptly.

Martha shifted her foot, prepared to nudge him instead of the laptop case with her toe. Or maybe not nudge him—maybe kick him. Hard. Why was he bringing up his tawdry past with Bruno's daughter?

Bruno didn't seem to mind. He beamed another fluorescent smile. "She's getting married next June."

"I know. She told me. The groom sounds like a great guy."

"He's not good enough for my baby. But then, no one is. Any chance you'll be in town long enough to get together with her? I'm sure she'd love to see you."

Martha worked hard to keep her face impassive. Modern affairs were beyond her comprehension. Modern fathers were beyond modern affairs. The last time she'd broken up with a boyfriend, her father had threatened to inflict bodily harm to him, even after Martha had insisted that she'd been the one to end the relationship and reassured her father that her heart wasn't even bruised, let alone broken. She couldn't begin to imagine her father saying, "Gee, why don't you and Richard get together the next time he's in town?"

"I was thinking I'd send her and the lucky guy a few cases of Blake's Brews once they make it legal," Blake said.

"She'd love that."

"Yeah." Blake smiled slyly. "Especially since she won't be able to purchase Blake's Brews in your stores."

Bruno tilted his head, a small bow of concession. Then he launched into another long-winded discourse on his inventory woes and his need for quick turn-around in his stores because, after all, the essence of health food was freshness. He pontificated on the soft drink industry in general, on carbonation and bottled water and glass versus plastic versus aluminum cans. Every now and then, one of his "veeps" would supply a figure or offer a clarification, but mostly it was Bruno Thompson's show. Blake and Martha listened courteously, but she wondered if he was as irritated by the lecture as she was.

Eventually Bruno slowed to a halt like a watch spring in need of rewinding. Next to her Blake shifted in his chair, his legs stretching under the table while his fingertips tapped quietly against its polished veneer. Closing her eyes, Martha visualized him in his usual apparel—T-shirt and jeans, or maybe a Hawaiian-print shirt and loose-fitting khakis. His discomfort now, trapped in an unforgiving chair and listening to Bruno's bombastic oration, was only magnified by his more formal attire.

She peeked at him. He stared at Bruno but said nothing. She didn't know whether he couldn't think of any more arguments or Bruno's speech had simply hypnotized him into a stupor.

She decided it was time for her to speak up. "Innovation," she said.

Bruno favored her with a mildly curious, mildly contemptuous glance. "What?"

"One way to keep customers coming back is with innovation," she said. She was winging it, unable to remember much of the few business-overview classes she'd taken in college that might have covered marketing strategies. "Customers like the old things, but they're also eager to try new things. Especially customers like yours. They're cutting edge. Health conscious and taste conscious. If you keep stocking the same items on your shelf, your stores are going to stop seeming cutting edge."

Bruno lapsed into thought. Martha peeked at Blake again, and found him peeking back at her, a faint smile curving his lips.

One of Bruno's male deputies spoke up: "I don't think anyone can contend that Good Earth isn't stocked with cutting-edge foods."

"If you could call food cutting edge," the female executive noted.

"It should be," Martha said. "Your chain is in the vanguard. You ought to be the first retailer in the Midwest to sell Blake's Brews. You don't want to be scooped by some stodgy supermarket chain, do you?" She wondered whether she should have implied, however vaguely, that other Midwestern retailers were considering carrying Blake's Fruit Brews. She tried to remember anything she might have learned in college about fudging during negotiations, shading the truth, conning the opponent.

Whatever the ethics of the situation, the strategy seemed to work. Bruno flickered his eyebrows up and down, then craned his head to stare at the ceiling. "I don't want to be scooped," he muttered. "You know, the big chains are carrying roasted soy beans now. They're carrying stone-ground whole wheat flour and organically grown vegetables. They're still the stores your grandmother shopped in, but they think tossing a few nouveau products on the shelves is going to make them hip. We've got to out-hip them."

"And Blake's Brews is a good way to do that," Martha asserted. "Take a small order. See how it does—"

"No," Blake cut her off. "Take a large order. You won't be sorry. This stuff will fly off the shelves."

Bruno's gaze seesawed between them. "We'll think about it," he said.

Blake took that as his cue to stand. Martha hurriedly stood, too, and then all the other men at the table dutifully stood. "Think about it, then," Blake urged Bruno, bravely extending his hand to Bruno for another bone-crunching handshake. "I think you'll see the wisdom of what Martha's saying." He named the hotel where they'd been staying and said, "We'll be here until tomorrow." Then he took Martha's half lie and made it whole. "We've got some other meetings set up while we're in the area."

"We'll get back to you soon," Bruno promised. "It's a pleasure seeing you, Blake. Those Cape Cod sea breezes seem to be agreeing with you."

"Thanks. The Chicago winds haven't hurt you much, either." Blake smiled, then lifted Martha's laptop case for her, touched his hand to the small of her back and escorted her out of the room.

He didn't speak until they were safely inside the elevator, heading down to the lobby. "You were good," he said, a hint of amazement in his voice.

She sighed. She might have bought them a second chance with Good Earth, but she didn't feel too happy about it. "I lied."

"No, you didn't. You just gave Bruno the opportunity to misunderstand you."

"You gave him a bigger opportunity. What meetings do we have set up?"

Blake shrugged. "I don't know. We could meet with

a restaurant waiter and get some lunch. We could meet with a ticket seller at a movie theater and take in a flick."

"We're here on business," she reminded him sternly. She was the one who would have to calculate and file the expense reports for this trip.

"Well, we're just going to wind up waiting, one way or the other. I'm guessing if Bruno gets back to us, it won't be until midafternoon. Then we'll have to get him to sign a contract before he changes his mind again. We can wait at the hotel or we can wait in a movie theater. Your choice."

"Let's go back to the hotel to see if Doug called," she suggested. "After that…" Maybe she could go out to lunch with Blake, and to a movie. And it would seem like a date. She would feel like a smitten high-school wallflower, the way she'd felt that night he had driven her home in his classic convertible. She would blush and feel her palms sweat, and she would act like a tongue-tied ninny.

She wanted to believe that she'd changed. Her mystery visitor had altered her that night, changed her perspective and convinced her of her own womanly strength. She wanted to believe she would never feel nervous and infatuated around Blake again. So far she'd handled herself pretty well with him on this trip. She'd been painfully aware of how attractive he was, but she hadn't made a fool of herself.

But they hadn't gone to a movie together.

"Okay," he agreed. "Let's go back to the hotel and check our messages." He flagged down a cab outside the building, and within ten minutes they were back at the hotel. A message was waiting for them—but it wasn't the one they'd expected.

Blake unfolded the hotel's printout of the message, read it and grinned. Then he handed it to Martha.

"We want exclusive rights to distribute Blake's Fruit Brews in the Chicago region," it said in computer type. "Let's work it out. Bruno."

She wasn't sure how Blake would feel about giving Bruno exclusive rights, even if only for a limited period of time. But when she handed the message back to Blake, she got a pretty clear idea. He was smiling, a slow, mischievous, inexcusably sexy smile that made her heart skitter, even though she knew the inspiration of that smile was Bruno's capitulation. It had nothing to do with her.

But then Blake grabbed her, so swiftly she couldn't back away. He gathered her into a hug, lifted her off her feet and swung her in a circle. "Oh, Martha," he murmured. "You *were* good. You *are* good. You did it!"

And she knew his smile had at least a little to do with her, after all.

6

THE MOVIE STANK. It featured car chases, explosions and a plot with more holes in it than a chunk of Swiss cheese. The actresses were good-looking but they kept their clothing on, so they didn't add as much entertainment value as they could have.

Despite the movie's flaws, though, Martha seemed to be enjoying herself. She and Blake had decided to skip lunch and head straight to the theater, where he'd bought a jumbo tub of popcorn for them to share. He could do business lunches when he had to, and business meetings, too. But when he had to kill a few hours—no way were they going to respond too quickly to Bruno's message, especially after fibbing about having other meetings on their schedule—he'd figured a spy thriller was as good a way to spend time as sitting in a fancy restaurant somewhere, making idle conversation.

He wasn't really good at idle conversation. He suspected that Martha wasn't good at it, either. He hadn't guessed she'd be good at watching a schlocky movie in the middle of a business trip, snickering at the stilted dialogue and rolling her eyes at the clichés, but to his surprise, she was quite good at it. She also seemed to be good at surprising him.

The theater was less than half-full, and he and Martha were easily the most formally dressed people in the audience. The majority of the audience seemed to be retirees—who else could go to a matinee on a weekday?—and none of them had on tailored suits or blazers. None of them sat as straight as Martha, or held their heads as proudly. None of them laughed the way she did.

She had a wonderful laugh. It was quiet, bubbling up from her throat and emerging low and lilting. She had a wonderful profile, too. A couple of times, her fingers brushed his as they reached for a handful of popcorn simultaneously, and he realized that she had wonderful hands, the skin soft, her nails filed smooth and polished with a neutral glaze.

He was glad she'd agreed to go to the movies with him. It was unscheduled and inappropriate, but she'd risked her reputation as a by-the-books bookkeeper and nodded when he suggested taking in a flick.

He'd never before thought of her as a risk taker—he'd always assumed accountants were the very antithesis of risk takers—yet she'd taken a big risk when she'd opened her mouth at the meeting with Bruno that morning, and her risk had paid off. He liked that. When it came to women, risk taking outranked a sexy figure or pouty lips on Blake's excitement scale, every time.

There he was again, thinking about Martha in unexpected ways. And why not? She *was* exciting. Her legs, her laugh, her courage at the meeting with Bruno... Martha, the number cruncher, excited him.

On the screen, the hero and heroine were locked in a steamy clinch, kissing in a strangely mechanical way. Blake wondered what Martha would have said if the movie had been rated R instead of PG-13, and if the rating had been due to sexual content rather than violence and foul language. As the hero and heroine continued to slobber and tongue each other, he glanced at her in the theater's gloom. She looked bored. He couldn't blame her; as cinematic kisses went, this one was pitiful.

He wondered how she kissed. No woman had ever looked bored after kissing him—but Martha wasn't like any other woman he'd ever kissed. Would she be firm and resistant or soft and yielding? Would he have to seduce her gently and gradually, or would she melt and open to him?

Just thinking about it got his blood pumping. He shifted the popcorn tub on his lap and turned back to the screen. The kiss had been interrupted by the arrival of a fleet of police cars, fire engines and other emergency vehicles, all of them flashing their lights. Their sirens seemed almost like a personal warning to Blake, a reminder that if he kept thinking about Martha in the context of sex, he was going to need a fire engine to hose him down.

What had happened to his plan to match her up with Doug? Poor guy—his father fell ill, and what did Blake do? Fantasize about the woman he'd thought would be perfect for Doug. Maybe Doug wasn't interested in her, though. Maybe she wasn't interested in Doug. Maybe fate had intervened for a reason. Sometimes things turned out for the best.

They still had nearly half a tub of popcorn left when the movie ended. Blake dumped it into a trash can on the way out, and Martha stopped at the snack stand to get a napkin, which she used to wipe the butter off her fingers and lips. Blake would gladly have kissed the butter off her lips—and for the umpteenth time, he gave himself a silent scolding for considering Martha in the context of sex. She was his accountant, for crying out loud, he thought with a sigh as she turned from the snack stand and smiled at him.

"It's three-thirty," she said. "Do you suppose we should put Bruno out of his misery?"

Blake almost blurted out that he wouldn't mind being put out of his own misery—with a leisurely, butter-flavored kiss. But the whole idea was so crazy. He nodded brusquely and turned from her, reaching for the glass door and holding it open so she could exit ahead of him.

They blinked and squinted like moles emerging into the pale afternoon sunlight. The hotel was a three-block walk from the theater, and Blake suppressed the urge to take her hand as they strode briskly down the windswept sidewalk. He allowed himself to touch her back when they entered the crosswalk, but if she felt his hand on her she didn't acknowledge it, and he let his arm fall as soon as they reached the opposite curb. They didn't talk; there was too much traffic noise and they would have had to shout.

At the hotel, they boarded the elevator. "That was a stupid movie," Martha said.

"It didn't make much sense," he agreed.

"The whole idea—that the future of the planet depended on one single envelope reaching the president—was preposterous. But even if you accepted the premise, the agents were so careless! It would have been so simple for one of them to courier the envelope to the White House, instead of roaming all over the world with it."

"Yeah, well..." He grinned. "Movies like that are supposed to give you a rush, not get you to think."

"I guess I can't help thinking," she said, almost apologetically.

"Thinking is good," he conceded. Most of the time it was good, he added silently. Sometimes thinking could get you into big-time trouble, though. Sometimes *not* thinking could get you into even worse trouble. He didn't know whether he was better off thinking or not thinking when it came to Martha.

The elevator bumped gently as it stopped on their floor. They ambled down the hall together until they reached her door. Blake paused with her as she reached for her key, then remembered that he had to walk two more doors to get to his own room. He had to force himself to keep going; it seemed natural for him to enter her room with her.

He was really insane. Mentally mutated. This was *Martha Cooper*, and he wanted to join her in her room and demonstrate the difference between that chewy, grotesque big-screen kiss they'd witnessed in the movie and a *real* kiss, a kiss with passion, a kiss that would burn them both up from the inside out.

The very idea that he could link Martha and passion in his mind shook him. Yet there it was. He wanted her.

He marched to his own door, shoved his computerized keycard into the slot, yanked the lever and barreled into his room, hell-bent on keeping himself from U-turning and chasing back to her room. His reflection greeted him from the mirror attached to the bathroom door. He looked normal to himself, except for the atypical outfit he was wearing. It was Blake Robey's face, though, Blake Robey's body, Blake Robey's eyes staring back at him from the glass. He hadn't changed.

Martha had. Nothing he could put his finger on, nothing specific or concrete. She hadn't gained or lost any weight, hadn't altered her hairstyle, hadn't dressed differently. But even so...

Just thinking about her made him hard.

He stalked farther into his room to get his files so they could return to Good Earth and put the deal together. The flashing red light on his phone caught his attention. He lifted the receiver and punched the message button.

"Hi, Blake, it's Doug," came the voice-mail message. "I just got a free minute. My dad's stabilized and they're going to do bypass surgery on him, probably tomorrow. The prognosis looks good. I just wanted to let you know. I hope you haven't botched things too badly with Bruno."

No, I haven't botched things too badly with Bruno, Blake growled to himself, although he was pleased to hear Doug's father was doing okay. If he hadn't botched things, it was probably because Martha had saved the day. She'd stretched the truth and finessed Bruno. Without her—

Without her, Blake would have done fine, he assured himself. He had to stop thinking she was a sorceress, casting spells on Bruno and on Blake himself. For God's sake, she was Martha the accountant.

He hung up, then dialed her room. When he heard her voice, low and a little husky, he almost believed she was a sorceress again, warming his blood as he pictured her licking the salty butter off her fingers in the movie theater. He cleared his throat before speaking. "I got a message from Doug. His father's holding his own."

"Oh, that's wonderful!" Even full of cheer, she sounded sultry to him.

"They're going to do a bypass tomorrow."

"Oh," she said, sounding a bit more subdued. "That's major surgery."

"Yeah, but it's been done a million times. I'm sure he'll be okay."

"I hope so."

Did she sound wistful? As if her thoughts were completely with Doug? As if she wished she could be with him right now, holding his hand and helping him through the ordeal? Did she even have a hint of what Blake was thinking about when he thought about her? Did she have the slightest clue?

If she did, would she run screaming in the opposite direction?

"So. Are you ready to go see Bruno?" he asked.

"Sure."

"Okay." He wanted to say he'd knock on her door to get her, but he was afraid that if he knocked and she opened it, he might step inside. "I'll see you in a minute," he mumbled, then hung up.

He had to get a grip, had to pull himself together and act cool. They were heading off to negotiate a contract, and she was thinking noble thoughts about Doug's father, and Blake was the president of a corporation and had to act accordingly. He had to be an executive, professional, in control. This wasn't party time and she wasn't just some lady who turned him on.

He'd get the deal done, period. That was the only goal he could let himself think about.

TWO HOURS LATER, they left the Good Earth headquarters and exited into a dark, blustery rush hour. The sky had a purplish glow and cars streamed down the avenue in chains of white headlights and red taillights. Blake was carrying her laptop along with his own portfolio of signed documents.

Somehow, miraculously, they'd won the Good Earth account, without having to make too many concessions. She felt giddy, thrilled to be a part of the company's first huge foray into national distribution and dazed that she'd managed to contribute to the accomplishment.

She'd thought Blake would be ecstatic. He seemed pleased, but somewhat muted as he searched the heavy traffic for an unoccupied cab.

"We should do something special for dinner," she suggested, because he didn't seem in a festive enough mood. "We need to celebrate."

He glanced down at her. A gust of wind tangled his hair, lending his face a boyishness that made her go soft inside. It almost wasn't fair that he should be so handsome and so successful and yet so utterly unegotistical, so unaware of his own appeal.

"What do you have in mind?" he asked her. A light flickered in his eyes. If she were a femme fatale, she might believe that light held an interest that went beyond a special dinner. She might believe the energy humming through him had less to do with landing a huge distribution deal than with her.

But she couldn't believe that. "I don't know," she said. "Some interesting restaurant, I guess."

He ruminated on her answer, then shrugged and waved at a cab weaving through the traffic. "I don't know much about Chicago restaurants. I suppose we could go back in and ask Bruno, or maybe stop back at the hotel and talk to the concierge."

"Let's be adventurous," Martha said, surprising herself. She wasn't an adventurous sort. The only time she'd been truly adventurous had been last summer— when she'd wound up accepting a position with Blake's Fruit Brews. And maybe that Saturday night when she'd received the gift of one magical hour, although that hadn't really happened. She'd only been adventurous in her imagination that night.

Still, the occasion called for festivity. As the cab veered to the curb, she climbed in, Blake behind her, and called to the driver through the Plexiglas partition: "Excuse me—could you recommend a restaurant?" Blake eyed her curiously, but he was smiling.

The cabby turned in his seat. "A restaurant?"

"Your favorite place. Where you'd go if you had something to celebrate," she explained. She glanced at Blake to make sure she wasn't overstepping her bounds. His smile grew and his eyes shimmered.

The driver thought for a moment. He peered into his rearview mirror; Martha saw his reflection in the rectangular glass. He was frowning dubiously. "Where I'd go," he said in accented English, "not where I think you'd go."

"We're open-minded," she insisted, astonished and honestly pleased by her recklessness. "Take us there and we'll decide."

"Okay. Is your dollar," he conceded, flicking the lever to start the meter and easing into the flow of traffic.

Twenty minutes later, they might have been in another city—possibly even another world. Gone were the glass-and-steel skyscrapers, the self-important business professionals charging along the sidewalks with their leather carryalls. The cabdriver cruised slowly through a jumbled ethnic neighborhood of walk-up apartments and corner groceries, Laundromats and liquor stores. He pulled to a halt in front of a stairway that led down a short flight to a door with Marta's painted on it. "Down there," he said. "Is best food in all the city."

Martha and Blake exchanged a look. She felt a twinge of apprehension, but his gaze seemed to dare her. "It's got your name on it, almost," he pointed out.

"Okay," she said, determined not to shrink back into her proper accountant persona. "Let's give it a try."

Blake paid the driver. "Will we be able to get a cab here when we're done?" he asked, surveying the colorful neighborhood.

"Oh, sure, lotsa cabs. You tell Marta to call if you can't get one, I come back," he promised. "You tell her, call T.J. She'll get me."

Gathering her courage, Martha let Blake help her out of the cab. He smiled again, this time looking amused and intrigued all at once. "You've got guts," he murmured, taking her hand and leading her to the stairs.

"I hope I still have guts after eating whatever they serve at this joint," she joked, determined to stay as gutsy as she'd felt when she'd gotten into T.J.'s cab.

They descended the stairs and entered an atmospherically dark eatery. The decor was minimal—tables, chairs, a few trite landscape prints hanging on the walls. Chatter filled the air from diners occupying most of the tables. None of them seemed to be dressed in business clothes.

A woman came over, held up two fingers and beckoned them with a nod. She sat them at a tiny table in a corner, handed each of them a menu and disappeared.

Bracing herself, Martha lifted her menu. It was written in a language she'd never seen before. A startled laugh escaped her. "What is this? Bulgarian?"

"Something Slavic, I'd guess," Blake agreed, joining her in laughter. "Any idea what the menu says?"

"None whatsoever." At least she could read the prices next to the foreign-language listings. They were significantly lower than anything she and Blake could have found in a sandwich shop in the neighborhood of their hotel.

He laughed harder. She laughed, too, a helpless, carefree, what-the-hell laugh. When a waitress came over with water, Blake handed her their menus and said, "Just bring us your best dishes. And wine. We'll take our chances." The waitress nodded and departed, and Blake leaned toward Martha. "Was this what you had in mind as a celebration?"

"I think…" His hands were on the table, just inches from hers. If she leaned toward him, they could link fingers. Her gaze could touch his. The mere thought made her pulse flutter. "I think sometimes you have to take a chance," she said. "Not always, but sometimes."

"I'm a big fan of taking chances." He closed the distance, covering her hands with his. His palms were warm and large, protective and possessive at the same time. She felt heat rush through her veins at his touch, but also something more, something that assured her he was glad she'd taken this chance.

It occurred to her that she was taking a bigger chance by letting him touch her than she had by allowing the cabdriver to bring them to this underground café. Yet she felt safe with him, safe enough to stop caring whether she was safe.

The waitress returned to their table with a bottle of wine and two plates, one with what appeared to be shredded, pickled cucumbers and olives, and another with strips of smoked fish topped by a pale sauce. She poured some wine for them, then vanished.

Blake released Martha's hands and reached for his glass. "A toast," he said, lifting it.

She lifted hers as well. "Here's to a successful negotiation with Good Earth," she said, tapping her glass against his.

"Here's to you," Blake murmured, then sipped.

To her?

If Martha were more practiced in male-female relationships, she'd know the strange radiance illuminating his eyes meant nothing. But she was inexperienced enough to think that just maybe that glow had something to do with desire.

Not that Blake Robey could possibly desire her. But...it almost looked that way. It almost seemed it from the way he continued to gaze at her.

The wine tasted good—dry but with an exotic nutty flavor. That gave her courage to taste the minced cucumber. Blake bravely cut a piece of the fish with the edge of his fork and popped it into his mouth.

"Ooh!" she said.

"Wow!" he said simultaneously.

They both laughed again.

Every dish the silent waitress brought them was exquisite. They shared plates of salty noodles, spiced meats, stewed vegetables and chewy breads. They munched on pastries and cheeses. They sipped their wine. And they talked—about Blake's beloved vintage Mustang, her sister, his sister, his first resort job as a teenage townie on the Cape, her first job bagging groceries when she'd been in high school. They talked about Lucy and about the last dog he'd had, who had died two years ago and whom he still missed.

It was not the celebratory dinner she'd expected. It was better.

And the best part of all was how good it was to talk to Blake, and how relaxed she felt with him. No adolescent nerves, no sweaty palms, no panic. He was like a friend, a soul mate, someone she'd known forever, intimately.

The magic didn't end after Blake paid the absurdly small bill. They stepped outside and their cab was waiting for them, with T.J. behind the wheel.

Blake didn't speak once they were settled in the cab. He didn't have to. The gap of space between them that Martha had been so conscious of that morning was now bridged by their arms, her hand clasped within his. At any other time, she would have been astonished to find herself holding hands with Blake in the back seat of a cab. But tonight it seemed natural. Inevitable.

She had no idea what was going to happen once they got back to the hotel. If the closeness they'd shared over dinner was real, if the strength and warmth of his hand holding hers meant anything, what would happen at the hotel was obvious. But she was Martha Cooper, and he was the luscious hunk of a boss who'd viewed her as nothing more than a competent accountant for the past four months, and if she could lapse into a weird dream state once, why not twice? For all she knew, this entire evening was an illusion. She would probably wake up tomorrow in her own bed in Hyannis, with Lucy outside her bedroom door, yapping to go outdoors, and she would realize she'd dreamed the entire thing: the flight to Chicago, Doug's father's heart attack, the successful courting of the Good Earth executives, the restaurant with the mute waitress and the indecipherable menu. The cab ride back to the hotel. Blake's hand enveloping hers.

It could all be a dream.

Or a gift.

T.J. coasted up the circular driveway and under the awning to the hotel's front door. Blake paid the amount on the meter, then handed the driver a twenty dollar bill and said, "Thanks." The driver seemed neither startled nor embarrassed by the huge tip. He simply nodded, as if he understood why Blake was so grateful to him.

Hand in hand, they walked through the carpeted lobby to the elevators. Hand in hand, they rode up to their floor. Hand in hand, they sauntered down the corridor to her door—and then Blake drew her past it, past the door that had once been Doug's, and halted at his door. He inserted his keycard, watched the green light on the door plate flash, and tugged the lever to open the door. Then he turned to her.

She could wake up now. She could smile and say, "Fabulous dream, but now it's time for reality." Or she could let Blake have his way with her the way her dream man had during that heavenly hour that had realigned her clock at the end of daylight saving time.

Neither alternative appealed to her. She didn't want to wake up, but she didn't want to move through the dream like a passive sleepwalker, either. If this was her dream, she was going to be an active agent in it.

Rising on tiptoe, she touched her lips to his. Just a light brush of kiss, nothing aggressive, nothing that would burn away the dream with scorching heat, nothing that would scare a man away. Nothing that would result in corporate hysteria—the boss and the accountant in a torrid embrace!—and wind up costing her her job. Just a little peck of friendship and gratitude and—

He hauled her into his arms, covered her mouth with his, and notions like friendship and gratitude evaporated from her mind. He kissed her the way her dream man had kissed her, only it seemed more real, more true. She felt wide-awake, acutely aware, intensely, astonishingly alive as his energy infused her. His arms were so strong, his kiss so greedy, his body so hard and hungry.

She didn't remember moving, but somehow they wound up in his room, the door closed behind them. He pulled back to catch his breath, and she had a moment to glimpse his face before he circled his arms around her once more and lowered his mouth to hers. *Blake*, she thought, half-dazed. Blake Robey—the man she'd had a crush on since the instant she'd entered his office one hot summer day, clutching the edition of the *Cape Cod Times* with his classified ad in it—wanted her. He wanted *her*.

That comprehension excited her almost as much as kissing him did. This wasn't love, it couldn't possibly be, but it was red-hot desire, and it was hers for this moment. Tonight she felt beautiful and desirable and unabashedly sexy. His kiss made her legs go weak beneath her, but it made her heartbeat strong.

Remembering the deep pleasure she'd taken in pleasing her mystery lover, she returned Blake's kiss, opening her mouth to him, tangling her tongue with his. She lifted her hands to the nape of his neck and twined her fingers through his soft golden hair. She wanted to make him groan, wanted to make him feel as weak and strong as she did. She wanted his heart to be beating like hers, his blood as searing as hers as it coursed through him.

He broke the kiss again, slid his hands up to her shoulders and eased back to look at her. His eyes glittered beneath sleepy lids and his lips were damp from kissing her. She wondered whether he thought this was all a dream—and if so, whether he wished he could wake up. But he only smiled, a slow, seductive smile that told her this dream wasn't going to be ending any time soon.

Catching her hand with his, he pulled her through the entry and to the main area of the room. Like her room two doors down, it featured a king-size bed and sturdy walnut furniture. The carpet was soft, the lamplight amber, the diaphanous drapes softening the galaxy of city lights on the other side of the glass. But she didn't want to waste time studying his room. She wanted to see only Blake.

His gaze remained on her face as he removed her jacket. He didn't need to glance down to find the buttons of her blouse, to pluck them open, to tug the tails from the waistband of her skirt. His eyes locked with hers, he ran his hands over her exposed midriff, up to her bra, around to the back where the clasp was. He unhooked it and eased it, along with her blouse, down her arms.

Her heart began to beat faster, and her legs began to feel weaker. This was too real to be a dream. She was being stripped naked by a man who'd been the lover of her dreams for months, a man whose appearance and smell and touch seemed identical to the dream lover who had visited her in her room one magical Saturday night.

He tossed her blouse and bra onto the nearest chair, then brought his hands back to her, stroking from her waist up her spine to her shoulders, along her collarbones and down to her breasts. She arched into his touch, dazzled by the warmth and tenderness in his fingers as they explored the curves of her flesh. Her nipples swelled against his thumbs as he chafed the sensitive skin. He backed up to sit on the bed, bringing her with him, and took one nipple into his mouth.

Her breath caught in her throat. She combed her fingers into his hair, holding his head to her, wishing he had removed his clothing first so she could caress him as he was caressing her. She forced herself to release him and attack his jacket, shoving it off his shoulders and down his arms. He stopped kissing her long enough to help her remove it, then turned his attention to her other breast, kissing, licking, gently grazing his teeth over the nipple.

She wanted to moan, wanted to sigh and cry and tell him how much this meant to her, how good it felt. But like her dream, this moment didn't have room for words. It was all sensation, all heat and yearning and need.

She worked at the buttons of his shirt, nowhere near as deft as Blake when it came to the task of disrobing a lover. She didn't want to think about how much practice he'd had at disrobing his sex partners over the years. She didn't want to think at all.

She continued to fumble with the buttons, hoping he would help her and smiling when he finally nudged her hands away and opened the shirt in one sweeping motion. He shrugged out of it and flung it across the room.

The rest of their clothing seemed to vanish more quickly—her skirt dropping to her ankles, his belt buckle opening with a click of brass against leather, her half slip whispering against her stockings, his socks flying through the air, one landing on the luggage stand and the other on the TV cable box. His trousers, her panties, his boxers...everything gone in less than a minute, leaving her naked and vulnerable before him—and leaving him naked and as magnificent as a classic sculpture of some Olympian god, worthy of worship.

She would worship him, all right—with her gaze, her hands, her mouth. She would seize this opportunity to love Blake.

He pulled her down onto the bed beside him and she wrapped her arms around him, amazed at how real he felt, how solid and alive. She felt the strength and firmness of his muscles, the satiny warmth of his skin, the rapid drumming of his heart as she moved her hands over his chest. A light dusting of golden hair coated the skin, and she explored its texture with her fingertips, twining through the curls to reach his nipples. They tightened when she touched them, and tightened even more when she slid her hands down to his abdomen.

He shifted, using his legs to turn her onto her back, and pressed a fierce kiss to her lips. His breath was harsh, uneven, but still he didn't speak. Nor did she, not when he slid one leg between hers, not when he cupped one hand around her bottom and pressed her against his thigh. Not when he abandoned her mouth to kiss her shoulder, to brush a streak of kisses down between her breasts. Not when his fingers dug into her hip and he rocked her against him and she wanted to beg him to hold her even closer, to kiss her even deeper.

He rose above her, propping himself on one hand while the other roamed freely over her body, tracing the arch of her ribs, the angular edges of her hip bones, the thatch of hair between her thighs, the moist flesh below. He slid one finger into her and she choked on a sigh, refusing to shatter the silence. She brought her hands to him, arousing him as he aroused her, rubbing the rigid length of him as he readied her for him. *Blake*, her heart whispered as she clamped her hands on his hips and pulled him down. *Blake*, her soul called out as she opened for him, guided him to her and waited, feeling the teasing heat of him, sensing the tension in him as he held back, still stroking her with her hands, bathing her in her own dampness until she was afraid she would peak before he'd even entered her.

He peered down into her eyes. He must have seen her desperation in her face, because at last he drew his hand away and thrust into her. A broken breath escaped him as he rested for a moment inside her, letting her grow accustomed to him.

She didn't need time to grow accustomed. He fit her as if she'd been designed just for him, her body all his, only his. He bowed to kiss her and thrust again, adopting a slow, merciless rhythm. He felt so good. Divine. Like a dream.

Her body matched his, surged to meet him, became lost in the sheer ecstasy of having him inside her. Her thighs ached with pleasure, her hands gripped his back, she turned her head and offered him her throat to kiss. He pressed his mouth to the hollow of her neck and she convulsed inside, her body throbbing around him. She bit her lip, but not before a single word escaped: "Blake..."

"Martha," he groaned, and for that one instant, hearing her name on his breath as he climaxed inside her, she could actually believe this wasn't a dream.

7

BLAKE FELT BETTER. A lot better. For the first time in weeks, he actually felt...*sane*.

More than sane, of course. He felt incredibly powerful, and surprisingly helpless. He felt sated, yet starving for more. He felt as if he'd just discovered all of life's secrets in Martha's arms—and as if he didn't know a damned thing at all.

Maybe he also felt crazy, along with sane.

Martha. Wonder infused him as he rolled onto his side, his arms wrapped around her, and peered into her face. Her cheeks were flushed, her lips shaped in a delectable pout. The elegant hollow at the base of her throat rose and fell with each ragged breath. Her eyelids were half-lowered, but her eyes were on him, dark and simmering.

He slid one of his hands down her arm to capture her hand. Lacing his fingers through hers, he thought about how those fingers had felt floating across his skin, warm and wicked. How they'd felt arousing him, sliding up and down the length of him and then skimming the tip, where he was most sensitive.

His groin muscles clenched. Good grief, he was starving for more. More of Martha. Only Martha.

His accountant.

He laughed.

Her eyes widened. "What are you laughing at?"

"Don't you think this is kind of funny?" he asked, then tightened his grip on her hand when he saw the flash of indignation in her eyes. "I mean," he added quickly, not wanting to offend her, "in your wildest dreams, did you ever imagine you and me ending up in bed together?"

She didn't answer immediately.

"I mean, it's great," he explained, when her silence had extended beyond a full minute. "Funny, but great." God, that sounded lame, even to himself.

"Uh-huh," she grunted.

"Phenomenal." His smile died as he acknowledged how true that was. Sex with her had been phenomenal. Incredible. Better than anything he'd ever experienced before. His groin muscles contracted again, just from the memory of how spectacular it had been.

He studied her expressive mouth, her thick lashes, her nose, her dark, glossy hair. "I mean it," he murmured, leaning forward on the pillow they shared and planting a light kiss on the tip of her nose. "Maybe I've been imagining us in bed, too. Maybe it was subconscious, and I just didn't recognize it. But for a while now, Martha...I've been watching you and thinking, 'There's more than just a great brain in there.'"

"Thank you." She still sounded insulted.

"I've been thinking about you at strange times, when I ought to be thinking about other things. Like— like this morning, when I should have been thinking about the meeting with Bruno, I was thinking about your legs."

"My legs." She frowned.

"Come on," he goaded her. "I'm telling you, the attraction has been there for a while, just beneath the surface. I'm glad it finally came out."

"Is that what this is about? Attraction?"

"Yeah." And sanity. And insanity. And chemistry. And craving. "You have great legs. And the rest of you is pretty damned amazing, too."

At last she softened, her mouth curving into a reluctant smile. "Oh, yes, I'm amazing."

"You are."

"You sound like a man who thinks he's under some obligation to shower a woman with compliments after he's done ravishing her."

"I'd rather ravish you again," he said, and his erection angled up another few degrees. "Forget the compliments. I'd rather just show you what I think of you." He ran his free hand from her shoulder down her side, past the dip at her waist to the rise of her hip. "You think you could stand doing this again?"

"Oh, I don't know," she said primly, and he knew she was joking now. Even as she maintained a straight face her eyes danced with amusement and arousal.

When had he first become aware of her face? he wondered. When had he first realized that she had such pretty eyes, such a kissable mouth, such soft cheeks?

He moved his hand forward, between her thighs, and she closed her eyes. A faint sigh passed through her parted lips and she opened to his touch. Like magic. Like he'd tripped a switch, released a latch and she was his.

The only problem, he admitted as he pressed his mouth to hers, was that he was hers at least as much. Merely watching her expression dissolve into that pose of erotic concentration was enough to snare him. Hearing the raggedness of her breath shackled him.

Seeing the slope of her back imprisoned him. He was the captive, Martha the jailer.

Easing onto his back, he lifted her on top of him. He wanted to feel her weight, her smooth, sleek flesh pressing down on him. He wanted to feel her hair spill onto his face and her breasts slide against his chest. He wanted her to ride him, to squeeze her thighs against his sides while he clamped his hands around her hips and locked himself inside her.

He pulled her down onto him. The warmth of her surrounded him, tight and wet, and his wish came true. Her hair rained down on him, her breasts rubbed against his chest and he filled his hands with the round flesh of her bottom and arched into her, again and again. Her fingertips bit into his shoulders, her breath emerged broken and he felt her nerves stringing taut, building in heat and energy, seeking release.

His own release was barely an instant away. After making love to her once, he should have had more staying power this time. But she felt too good. The lush strokes of her body around him, the rosy darkness of her nipples, her shuddering gasps and soundless moans as she welcomed his thrusts...

He was going to lose himself. Too soon. He was close to dying. The torture was too sweet.

He reached down to where their bodies met and touched her. She groaned, he touched her again and she was tumbling, sinking onto him as she came. He thought he heard her cry his name, and then he stopped thinking and let go in an almost painful rush, no longer himself, no longer anything but sensation.

She was still pulsing around him when he was done, her hands flexing on his shoulders, her breath raw and uneven across his cheek. His hand was trapped between them, but when he attempted to slide it free she groaned again, caught in a fresh climax that left her limp, emitting a choked sob of pleasure as her legs writhed against his.

He held her as she descended, waiting until her heart stopped thudding against his chest and her respiration returned to normal. Only then, when she settled against him with a contented sigh, did he speak. "You didn't think that was funny?"

"No," she sighed, shifting her head to his shoulder but remaining on top of him.

"Miserable, then," he said agreeably. "Tragic."

"Appalling," she helped out.

"Devastating."

She propped herself up at that. "Yes," she said, sounding oddly serious. "It was devastating."

He wondered once more if he'd offended her, if she was going to hate him for making jokes at a time like this. Women's brains were complicated, and Martha's was more complicated than most. Maybe it was because she spent so much of her time running numbers through computers, looking for balanced equations, analyzing profits and losses. Maybe she was assessing their lovemaking right now, running it through the computer of her emotions and trying to figure out the bottom line.

There was no bottom line when it came to sex. Yet he couldn't dismiss the possibility that she was already calculating her losses.

He tightened his arms around her, urging her head back onto his shoulder. He wasn't ready to make any grand pronouncements or commitments, but hell— this was good. It most definitely wasn't devastating.

He didn't know how to say that without sounding

corny or promising more than he intended to deliver. So he only held her, stroking her hair, trying to let her know without words that she was safe in his arms. She settled against him, her breathing steady, her hand flat against his breastbone and her body resting along his side, her legs sandwiching one of his. He was amazed at how sexy she was, even at rest. He would have to make love with her again, soon. Real soon.

He closed his eyes and let a wave of relaxation wash over him, as warm and soothing as sleep. When she stirred against him, he almost yelled at her to lie still. He was so comfortable with her lying on top of him, just like this.

"What time is it?" she asked drowsily.

He didn't open his eyes. "Who cares?"

"I do." She leaned back and he loosened his hold so she could prop herself up high enough to see the alarm clock on the night table. "Oh," she said quietly. "I'd better go."

That caught his attention. Opening his eyes, he scowled. "What are you talking about?"

"I just..." She pushed herself up to sit, blinking and raking her hair back from her face. "I just think I should go back to my room now."

"Why?"

"I just do." She twisted away, presenting him with her shoulder. He noticed a tiny beauty mark near her shoulder blade, and twin dimples at the base of her spine. He wanted to kiss her back, to touch it all over. He wanted to massage the muscles at the nape of her neck and reach around her from behind to fondle her breasts, and—

She swung her legs over the side of the bed, and the movement snapped him out of his reverie. He shot up into a sitting position, too, watching with confusion as she bent over to retrieve her panties. "What happened?" he asked, once again mystified by the strange functioning of a woman's brain. "What did I do wrong?"

"Nothing." She stepped into her panties, pulled them up and turned to give him an anxious smile. "Really, Blake. This was..." She sighed. "Unbelievable. But I just— I think it would be better if I went back to my own room to sleep."

"I don't think it would be better," he argued. "I think you should sleep right here."

"No." She turned away from him again, as if she were afraid to look at him. Searching the room, she spotted her bra on a chair and crossed to retrieve it.

"All right, look." He must have done *something* wrong. A woman didn't just bolt from a man's bed, acting as if he were toxic, after an interlude of extraordinary sex—unless something was wrong. For the life of him, he didn't know what was bugging her, but he couldn't stand the thought that he wasn't going to have her by his side all night.

He stood, approaching her cautiously, wishing he could read her mind. "Whatever I did, I'm sorry," he said, figuring an all-purpose apology couldn't hurt.

Her bra fastened, she spun back to him and offered a feeble smile. "You didn't do anything, Blake."

"I mean, when I laughed—I wasn't laughing at you. I was just laughing because the whole idea of you and me being so good together—"

"It *is* funny," she cut him off, dodging his outstretched hand and darting across the room to get her skirt. "It's bizarre. Completely illogical."

"Who cares? I sure don't," he insisted. All he cared

about was that she was planning to leave and he didn't want her to.

"Maybe..." She buttoned and zipped her skirt, then slid her arms through the sleeves of her blouse. "Maybe I just need some time to sort through my thoughts, okay?" she said with an unnaturally bright smile. Her eyes looked glassy. With panic or tears? He couldn't tell.

"What do you have to sort through?"

"Maybe I don't take this all as casually as you do." Her voice had an edge to it. Definitely panic. "Maybe I need to think."

"So think here. Who's stopping you?"

"Please, Blake..." Definitely tears, too. He saw one leak out the corner of her eye, and her voice wobbled a little. "I've just got to go, all right? It's my fault, not yours. Really." She scooped up her stockings and stuffed them into her laptop case, then wedged her bare feet into her shoes and snatched her jacket from the chair. "You did nothing wrong, Blake," she swore, startling him by giving him a swift, hard kiss on the lips before she raced out of his room.

He remained standing where he was, naked and be-wildered, staring at the closed door, at the emptiness of his room without her in it. Damn. He was feeling crazy again, but a whole different kind of crazy—the kind of crazy that came of believing he must have dreamed everything that had happened in the past hour. Because if what had happened had been real, Martha would have never run away.

WELL, NO ONE would ever accuse her of being a smooth operator. She dove inside her room, slammed the door shut and sank against it, letting her laptop case drop gently to the floor and then kicking off her shoes. Her heart was racing, her eyes watering, and she couldn't decide whether she'd just done the wisest or the stupidest thing in her life.

She could have spent the night with Blake. All night long, wrapped up in his arms, in his body. She could have spent the night sleeping with him and then awakened and made love with him and drifted back to sleep again.

But she'd looked at the clock on his nightstand and thought, *Uh-oh—I've been here almost a whole hour.* She'd been certain that at the end of the hour, the magic would disappear. The dream would be over. The gift would be gone.

She was an idiot, she decided grimly, scooping up her shoes and stalking into the room. Whatever had happened that daylight saving night had been a fantasy, a weird, mystical event. What had happened in Blake's room over the past hour had been decidedly down-to-earth and real. At least she *thought* it was real, when she wasn't thinking about how utterly impossible it was that Blake Robey would ever look at her twice, let alone look at her naked and like what he saw.

She lowered herself onto the bed and closed her eyes. What she'd just experienced felt real enough. The muscles in her thighs ached, and her lips still carried Blake's taste. Curling her fingers, she could imagine the texture of his hair as vividly as if she were running her fingers through it right now. Making love with him had been as real as everything else that had happened all day—successfully negotiating the Good Earth contract, taking in a dreadful movie, eating at that exotic restaurant with the indecipherable menu and coming home in their buddy T.J.'s cab. It was all real, no matter how unreal it seemed.

She had probably done the right thing in leaving Blake's room. He didn't love her. He wasn't going to devote himself to her, heart and soul. Chances were, by the time they got back to Hyannis, he'd be vaguely embarrassed by what they'd done in Chicago. He might even feel obligated to fire her, if he found that her presence at the firm made him uncomfortable. She might feel uncomfortable around him, too, and if she did she might leave on her own. Spending the night with him would only have increased the awkwardness between them when they woke up.

Yes, leaving his room had been a very wise move.

So why was she crying? Why did she feel bereft, sitting alone on a bed that was far too big for one person? Embarrassment she could handle, but heartbreak?

She couldn't have fallen in love with him. True, he had made love to her with more passion, more tenderness, more devotion than she'd ever received in her life—including dream experiences and gift hours—but she couldn't believe she'd crossed the line that separated having a crush from being in love. They'd gotten to know each other better today, and not just in bed. She'd learned a little about his love for his parents and his sister, and she'd seen him operating in a business context she'd never before witnessed. And they'd gone to a movie together, and his hand had collided with hers in the popcorn tub, and at dinner he'd scooped a taste of buttery herbed potatoes from his plate and extended it across the table so she could eat from his fork. She'd enjoyed his company. They'd grown friendly in a way they hadn't been before.

But it wasn't love. It couldn't be. He was a happy-go-lucky beach bum who had stumbled onto a unique product and found a way to market it. He was a Cape Cod boy, as sun-blessed and carefree as a California surfer. He was the stuff of infatuation, not love.

And he certainly didn't love her. He couldn't. She was not the sort of woman a man like Blake would fall in love with.

He had surely liked her while they'd been enjoying passionate sex—perhaps even liked her a lot. But once an hour was up, so was her gift. It was nothing she could count on for the long haul.

So she'd left, before the magic had a chance to slip away.

SHE WOULD HAVE LIKED to sneak out of the hotel the next morning without seeing him, but that was impossible. They were supposed to be leaving together, booked on the same flight back to Hyannis. Even if they weren't, she acknowledged, she couldn't elude him—because he was waiting for her by the elevators when she emerged into the lobby.

She hadn't slept well. To say she didn't look her best would have been euphemistic. Her eyes were ringed with shadow and her hair hung shaggy and rumpled.

It didn't make her feel any better to note that Blake looked wretched, too. Of course, on him, wretched was still unconscionably handsome. Clad in old, broken-in jeans, a nubby brown sweater and scuffed sneakers, he looked less like a business executive concluding an important trip than a kid from the neighborhood on his way to the local pub to have a beer and watch a football game on the wide-screen TV.

"Hi," he said. He sounded subdued, not his usual upbeat self.

"Hi." She focused on his chin so she wouldn't get trapped by his beautiful eyes.

"How about some breakfast before we check out?"

She wasn't hungry, but a cup of coffee might help. Wheeling her suitcase behind her, she nodded and followed him into the lobby café where they'd had breakfast the previous day.

A waitress seated them and Blake requested two coffees. Martha picked up her menu and stared at it blankly. All the dishes looked too robust and cheerful: eggs sunny-side up, a hearty stack of pancakes, the good-morning special. It was not a good morning, and she wasn't in a sunny mood. Her heart felt leaden.

"Coffee is all I want," she said when the waitress returned to take their orders.

Blake stared at her as if sensing a subliminal message behind her lack of appetite, then requested toast and juice. Apparently he wasn't all that hungry, either.

Lacking their menus to distract them, they were stuck with each other. Martha spent a significant amount of time unrolling her linen napkin and shaking out the silverware it contained, then spreading the heavy white square of cloth over her lap. She didn't have to look at Blake to know he was drinking his coffee, lowering his mug, lifting it again and drinking some more.

"Any word from Doug this morning?" she asked, deciding that one of them was going to have to act mature and get a conversation going—and it clearly wasn't going to be Blake.

"No."

"I hope everything's going all right with his father."

"Yeah."

So much for a conversation. She risked a glance at him. He was gazing past her at the waitress's station. He couldn't even look at her, she realized. He was feeling as uncomfortable as she was.

She considered raising the subject of last night, just to place it on the table where they couldn't ignore it. But what could she say? That it was *great*—his word— but she'd fled from him because she was afraid? Afraid of what? Getting too close? Finding out that his feelings for her were exactly what she thought they were—which was less than she wished they could be? Or finding out, even worse, that last night had been merely another one of those transient, inexplicable gifts, nothing lasting, nothing she could have faith in?

"I don't get it," he said abruptly, turning the full force of his eyes on her. "We were good together."

She traced the edge of her napkin with her thumb and took a deep breath. So he was the mature one, after all, pushing the subject out into the open. If he was brave enough to introduce it, she would be brave, too, and talk about it with him. "That was last night."

"We could have been good this morning, too."

They could have been better than good. Making love with Blake could have been like fireworks and rainbows and the *1812 Overture,* all rolled into one. "You're my boss," she said, because that seemed like the best way to explain away her apprehension.

"Your boss?" He frowned.

"Yes, my boss. The man who hired me. The man who runs the company I work for."

He swore under his breath, then leaned back as the waitress arrived with his toast and juice. Once she was gone, he hunched forward again, pinning Martha with his gaze. "What are you talking about? Am I going to find myself with a legal situation or something? One of those harassment charges? Because I didn't force anything, Martha. I think that's very clear."

She would have smiled if she didn't feel so glum. "I'm not going to sue you, of course not. I'm just saying, it's a bad idea for a woman to—to have an affair with her boss."

"You think this is going to change our working relationship?"

"Not if we let it just drop," she said. She heard a catch in her voice and sipped some coffee. "If we just pretend it never happened."

He buttered his toast thoughtfully. "Is that what you want to do?"

No! she longed to shout. She wanted to pretend it had happened, and it would happen again—it would happen every night. She wanted to pretend it was real—not only the sex but the emotions behind it, the intimacy, the need. She wanted to feel love for him and from him. "Yes," she answered.

"You want to just forget the whole thing ever happened?" He sounded bemused.

No. "Yes."

He shrugged. "If that's really what you want... Okay."

He obviously wasn't as troubled as she was. As long as he wasn't going to get sued, he could accept her position with a shrug and a bite of toast. By the time he'd finished his breakfast, he probably would have the entire incident erased from his memory bank.

Which was all the reason she needed to resolve that it would never happen again. If he could dismiss it, she would have to. Perhaps not as easily as he could, but it was done, over and she was going to have to move forward and not look back.

Like a dream, a gift, one more magical hour. She should accept the gift with grace and gratitude, and not feel bitter that it could never be anything more than that.

8

FOR THE LIFE OF HIM, he would never understand
women. Until now, that fact hadn't bothered him. But
now...

Martha.

He sat in his office just days after their return from
Chicago, Doug seated across from him in a well-
tailored suit, his loafers buffed and a copy of the Good
Earth contract spread open in his lap. "Bruno agreed
to this?" he asked, his eyebrows spiking with such
surprise his eyeglasses shifted. "How did you bring
him around? What did you do?"

"I don't know what I did," Blake muttered, although he knew damned well. What he'd done was sit
with Martha, her intelligence infusing him, her com-
posure keeping him calm and steady. Merely by being
together they'd become invincible, and they'd won
the day.

And then they'd celebrated. But he wasn't going to
think about that. She'd asked him to forget that celebration had occurred, and eventually, if he was very,
very lucky, he might be able to.

"I came up with some other ideas," Blake added,
causing Doug's eyebrows to jump again.

"What ideas?"

Blake leaned back in his chair and stared out the
window at the sleet-gray sky. He didn't want to share

his ideas just with Doug. He wanted Martha to hear them, too. He wanted her to realize what a genius he was.

He almost snorted at that. He was no genius. He hadn't even finished college, and there she was with her MBA. But even so—even if he was supposed to pretend she never had been and never would be any-thing but his company accountant—he wanted her to know that he got brainstorms.

"I thought, maybe we should have a meeting with senior staff to talk about some new markets I think we belong in."

Doug looked intrigued. "A staff meeting! Blake, this shows such responsibility and foresight. I'm proud of you."

Blake tried to make his grimace resemble a smile. Doug's teasing was only half in jest; the guy had never quite gotten used to Blake's informal way of running things. They rarely had staff meetings. The staff just sort of hung out and talked.

But he didn't want Doug to be proud of him. He wanted Martha... Hell, he just wanted Martha.

"So you got these ideas while you were away?" Doug asked. "What a productive trip. You were hot."

Only when Martha was with me, Blake thought bit-terly. And sure, they'd been hot together. In all kinds of ways.

Now she was avoiding him. She was somewhere in the building where he couldn't see her, couldn't find her. In her office, maybe, or the lounge, or the ladies' room—wherever he wasn't, that was where she was. One thing she definitely didn't want to be doing these days was hanging out and talking, at least not with him.

He couldn't really blame her. First, she was right about the whole boss-employee thing. If they had an affair, it could cause problems, resentments among the staff. Jealousy might flare up if she saw him swapping jokes with one of the secretaries, or she might screw up his profit-loss calculations with undetectable arithmetic errors if he decided to date another woman. It could get messy.

Second, and more important, she was probably looking for more in a relationship than Blake could offer. She wasn't like him, free and easy and footloose. She was a nice, quiet, well-bred woman, reserved and proper. He'd been astonished by the depth of her passion in Chicago, because most of the time she didn't come across as particularly passionate. She wasn't the sort of woman who fell into bed with a man just for fun. And Blake wasn't the sort of man who could promise a woman anything more than fun.

Okay. She was right. He had to forget the whole thing.

"So, where are we on the Midwest distribution center?" he asked Doug.

"We've got three Chicago area sites under consideration. There's an old water bottling plant for sale, which we could get up and running the fastest. I'm figuring we'll have to truck product to Good Earth for at least a while. I think we're better off leasing than buying the trucks, but if we lease we can't plaster Blake's Fruit Brews all over the sides."

"Why not? Can't we lease the trucks' sides as well as their cargo space?"

"I'll find out." Doug jotted a note to himself. "Once we've got a bottling plant set up in the Midwest, we can start looking into other Midwestern venues. It should work out well, since you gave Good Earth ex-clusive rights to sell our product for the first two years of the agreement, and only in Cook County. By the time the year is up, we'll be ready to expand in the Midwest." He beamed at Blake, obviously pleased. "I hope you're ready to make this move, Blake. This is the big time. You're not just a little entrepreneur in Hyannis anymore. You're going national."

"I'm going to Chicago," Blake retorted. He didn't feel big time. He didn't even feel little-time. He felt like what he was: a guy who, for the first time in his life, couldn't get the woman he lusted after.

He'd always gotten the woman before. He'd even gotten *this* woman once. But now he was turning into some hotshot mogul with a going-national company, and the woman was out of reach.

"What I'm saying is, it's a totally new mind-set for us," Doug explained. Blake wondered if this was the kind of thing they taught in business school. "There's going to be an extra zero or two on every number. Big-ger outlays, bigger income. Can you think big?"

Blake rolled his eyes. "What's your point, Doug?"

"I just want you to understand the gravity of the sit-uation." Doug fussed with the file again, even though it was perfectly neat. "You were talking about a senior staff meeting, which I think is something you ought to start holding on a regular basis. And you're going to have to expand the company's overall staff. I'm not just talking about truck drivers to cart the product out west. I'm talking about people who can monitor what's going on where. One of the biggest pitfalls of growth in a company is if the boss tries to hang on to his small-business mentality."

Blake had always assumed that expanding the business would mean that nothing changed except his income. He hadn't given much thought to hiring new staff. And for all he didn't like being lectured, he did respect Doug's expertise. "Who should I be hiring?"

"To start with, someone to watch those zeroes," Doug suggested. "A financial officer."

"I've got Martha," Blake said, then clenched his jaw to keep from cursing. He *didn't* have Martha, and he was tired of letting that truth bug him.

"She's an accountant. I think she could move up— she's got the skill—but you're going to have to promote her if you want her to take on more responsibilities. Give her a better title and a raise."

"Fine," he agreed. "I'll promote her." Doubt gnawed at him, though. What if she thought he was promoting her for personal reasons, because she'd slept with him—or because he wanted her to sleep with him again? What she'd said about having sex with her boss was right. It complicated everything.

"I don't know," he contradicted himself. "Maybe we'd be better off hiring someone else."

"I think Martha would be great for the position. She was with you in Chicago. She must have contributed to securing this deal with Good Earth. A promotion would be a nice reward, plus an acknowledgment that she's capable of much more than just figuring out the company's tax liabilities."

She'd contributed plenty to securing the deal. She did deserve the promotion. And regardless of sex, he believed she would do a better job as a financial officer than anyone else he could find for the position. She fit in well at Blake's Brews. She kept things running smoothly. She didn't get in his way or give him a hard time, except for her demanding that he forget the unforgettable.

"Okay. I'll offer the job to her."

"Smart move." Doug grinned. "She's going to be thrilled," he predicted. "In her own quiet way, she's a go-getter."

This was not a good conversation to be having. Blake knew about her own quiet way of getting, and giving. He knew enough about her to realize that any discussion of her was going to depress him. "I need a date," he muttered.

Doug had appeared on the verge of rising from his chair, but Blake's remark stopped him. "A date?"

Blake hadn't meant to say it out loud, but now that he had he couldn't retract it. "Yeah. A date. Me and a woman spending time together."

Doug frowned. "Do you want my help with that?"

Blake snorted. "No. I can get my own dates."

"I thought so." Doug stood and shook down the crisply creased legs of his trousers. "So get a date. You deserve one at least as much as Martha deserves the promotion."

Shut up about Martha! Blake wanted to snap. It seemed as if all conversational roads led to her—business growth, appropriate staffing, dates. If he asked Doug about turnips right now, Doug would find a way to include Martha in his answer: "Did you know she's got a fabulous turnip recipe? She cultivates turnips in her backyard. She was voted Turnip Queen at her high school."

The reason Blake needed a date was to erase Chicago from his memory, to remind him that there were plenty of women in the world, many of them sexier than prim, prissy Martha, many of them fully willing to make love and not run for cover moments after the deed was done. Many of them with better turnip recipes, too, he'd bet.

He needed a date to help him do the one thing Martha wanted him to do: forget her.

TWO GUYS from quality control were playing with the Velcro dartboard in the lounge when Martha went in to fix herself a cup of tea. As soon as it was brewed, she intended to bring it back to her office. She had grown skittish about remaining in the public rooms at Blake's Fruit Brews' headquarters. If she lingered in the lounge too long, she might run into Blake.

He obviously didn't want to see her. He knew where she was—at her desk, most of the time—and if he had anything to say to her, professional or personal, he was perfectly capable of contacting her.

His avoidance of her wasn't a sign of cowardice, though. It was sign of respect. She'd asked him to pretend nothing had happened between them in Chicago, and he was doing exactly that. He probably didn't even have to try; the entire incident had surely disappeared from his radar screen the minute they'd gotten off the plane at the airport in Barnstable and driven their separate ways home.

No, she was the cowardly one. She was the participant in that incident who couldn't make the memories disappear. She was the one who had spent every evening since her return from Chicago taking Lucy on long walks in the frigid night air, talking to the poor dog about why having sex with Blake Robey was wrong, even if it happened to be the fulfillment of her deepest fantasy. She was the one who lay awake late into the night, listening to the stillness of her house and wondering if someone, anyone—*Blake*—would visit her in her dreams. She was the one afraid to fall asleep, because if she dreamed about him, the dream would remind her of what could never be real.

She pulled her mug from the microwave and dipped a bag of peppermint tea in and out of the steaming water. Behind her she heard the thud of the Velcro balls hitting the target and the rasp of them being torn away from it. She heard the laughter of the quality control guys—Pete and someone whose name she couldn't remember—as they teased each other and competed. Life existed somewhere beyond her dreams, she remembered. Life, in the form of friendship and darts competitions and minty tea, was flowing along like a river. Sooner or later, Martha would find her way back into the stream. She'd shake off her silly schoolgirl moodiness and start paddling her canoe.

"Hey, Blake!" Peter exclaimed, causing her to flinch. Her fingers went numb and she dropped the tea bag's string into the cup. "I'm ahead by fifteen points. Wanna throw a few?"

"Hmm." She heard Blake's familiar voice, soft and textured, and it reminded her of the way he'd groaned when he was deep inside her, climaxing. She felt her cheeks grow feverish, and her fingers fumbled as she used a teaspoon to fish the tea bag out of her mug. "I'll pass," he said.

She hoped he would pass right by the lounge and keep walking down the hall, so she could escape and not have to see him. No such luck, though—she heard his footsteps behind her. They were softer than the laughter of the quality control guys, but her consciousness was so attuned to him, she could visualize his approach, even when she was facing away from him. She was acutely aware of his motions, his nearness, his shadow sliding over her back as he drew close. She saw the shadow skim the counter, and then he was standing next to her, searching the cabinet. "Tea?" he asked, eyeing her mug. "I thought you were a coffee drinker."

"Sometimes I prefer tea," she mumbled, sounding as uneasy as she felt.

He pulled a can of coffee and a box of filters from the cabinet and prepared the coffeemaker to brew. It wasn't unusual for him to make a fresh pot of coffee, even if he happened to be the founder and president of the company. That was his way—no pretensions, no airs, just doing what he chose without regard for how it would look to others. "Tea is a proper, ladylike drink," he observed, sending her a sidelong glance that she saw peripherally. "It's what little old spinster aunts drink."

He was goading her, and she hated him for it. "I'm drinking tea instead of coffee because the herbal tea has no caffeine in it. It won't keep me up tonight," she said coolly, just to prove he couldn't rattle her. Belatedly, she realized that she didn't want to be discussing sleepless nights with him.

His gaze shifted from Martha to the coffee dribbling into the decanter, and back again. "I'm giving you a promotion," he said abruptly.

"What?" Her fingers went numb again, and the spoon and the tea bag dropped onto the counter, spattering drops of tea across it.

"A promotion. Doug and I were talking. He thinks that with the company's growth, we need you taking on more responsibility."

She swallowed. What was he getting at? And why was he getting at it sideways, standing next to her in the lounge and staring at the coffeemaker? Why hadn't he come to her office or summoned her to his, so they could discuss this like the professionals they were? Why couldn't he act like her boss instead of a cute guy with a laid-back attitude?

"Don't read too much into it," he added. "I mean, it's strictly a business thing. The company needs a financial officer and you're my choice. It has nothing to do with...anything." He pulled a mug from another cabinet and set it down next to hers.

"Oh." She should have appreciated his clarifying that the promotion was not a personal issue, but it only made her blush again, remembering the personal issues that had burned so brightly between them in Chicago. She wiped the counter with a square of paper towel, then tossed it and the tea bag into the trash. "A financial officer?"

"Yeah. We could come up with a better title if you want. Controller? Comptroller? Whatever. All I know is, you're the best person we've got to handle the finances."

"I see."

"You've got the brains for it. You can handle it. There'll be a raise, too. I can have Doug and Penny from personnel go over it with you."

"Fine." The nerves at the nape of her neck tingled. Her hands felt damp. She was back to being a clumsy schoolgirl with him, and she hated it.

"You're looking good," he said, just as abruptly as he'd announced her promotion. She glanced hard at him and found him extremely fascinated by the coffeemaker. Maybe he'd been addressing the coffee, not her.

"Thank you." She forced out the words.

"That's a nice color." He waved vaguely at her blouse, a long-sleeved shell of teal silk tucked neatly into a pair of charcoal-gray slacks.

"Thanks." She didn't want him complimenting her, or her clothing. She didn't want to think he was aware enough of her to notice how she looked. It was flattering, but it sparked hope in her, and hope was a dangerous thing. What she hoped for—that Blake could be her dream man, that he could really care for her, that they could have more than an office fling, more than an unreal interval of lovemaking—wasn't going to come true, and she didn't want to be tempted by it.

"So, the promotion is okay with you?"

"The promotion is fine," she said. "I'll discuss it with Penny. I've got to get back to my office." If only she could come up with a clever line, a joke, something that would put them both at ease. Something that would prove she had done what she'd asked him to do and forgotten Chicago.

But she hadn't forgotten Chicago, and she wasn't clever. She picked up her mug and left the lounge, deciding she was every kind of fool there was.

TWO WEEKS LATER, Blake held his very first senior staff meeting. He didn't have a conference room like that stuffy room at Good Earth's headquarters, so they met in his office, with a few extra chairs dragged in.

Doug was there, of course, and Roger from product development, and Penny from personnel. Steven, the distribution manager, came armed with charts so he could present the options for Midwest regional distribution with visual aids. Blake's secretary, Helen, sat next to him, taking notes on her laptop.

Martha sat as far from Blake as she could without moving her chair out into the hall.

"I think our best bet is to purchase the bottling plant outside Chicago," Steven was saying. "The other two sites would entail much more extensive overhaul and construction. With this, we've got the machinery in place. The broker said we can probably get them to come down in price a bit. I'd like to fly out there and see it for myself."

"Good idea," Blake said. As far as he was concerned, it was a no-brainer, but he wanted to comport himself like a proper boss, levelheaded but enthusiastic.

"Maybe you'd like to accompany me?" Steven suggested.

"I think Doug can handle it. How's your father, Doug? Can you fly out to Chicago for a few days?"

"No problem," Doug said. "My father's doing fine. Complaining to my mother because she won't let him put salt and butter on his baked potatoes anymore."

Blake smiled and nodded, glancing surreptitiously at Martha. She sat primly in her chair, her knees together, one foot hooked behind the other ankle. She was wearing a skirt, though, and he couldn't help but admire her legs. Even though he shouldn't. Even though he knew she didn't want him to.

"You ought to talk to Martha about how much we're going to spend on this thing, what kind of loans it's going to take and all that stuff," Blake added, then silently scolded himself for saying "all that stuff." It sounded so unprofessional. "Martha, will you and Steve get together on that?"

"Of course," she said.

God, this group was smooth. A wonderfully functioning business organization. He felt like an adult. Did Martha notice? Did she care that he was acting like a genuine executive? Had she already gotten past it, forgotten everything and moved on with her life?

Blake was trying to. Last Saturday, he'd gone on a date with an old friend of his. They'd been close a few years back, but then they'd gone their separate ways. Blake had been fond of her, and he'd given her a call. He'd taken her to the Paddock for dinner, a big, pricy, fancy meal with wine and cognac and the works, followed by a movie at the Cineplex across from the mall. It had been a good movie, well-reviewed, with A-list actors. No explosions, no plot holes. Blake had hated it.

He'd driven her home afterward, listening and nodding as she analyzed the emotional impact of the movie. At her front door she'd invited him in and he'd said no. He liked her, she was beautiful, they'd had a grand time together when they'd been dating way back when, but he didn't want to make love with her.

Once again, all the symptoms pointed to his being insane.

"If we're done discussing the bottling plant," he said, "I want to run some ideas past you." Damn it, he was a good executive. He had good ideas. Martha had better notice. "I'd like to talk about moving Blake's Fruit Brews into other markets. Besides Chicago, I mean."

"That's not your department," Doug spoke up with a grin. "You're the creative genius. I'm the one who's supposed to have the marketing ideas."

Blake ignored him. "I was thinking, we ought to be

getting Fruit Brews onto airplanes. Those beverage carts have nothing worth drinking, other than booze."

"That's a great idea," Penny said.

Blake glanced at Martha, hoping she would think it was a great idea, too. She smiled enigmatically and jotted something on her leather-bound notepad.

"I think we might run into problems because the drinks are packaged in bottles," Doug pointed out. "If Blake's Brews came in cans, the airlines might be interested. But bottles are glass, and they're heavy."

"The Bloody Mary mix they use is in a glass bottle. Same with the wine and most of the other liquor. It's just the soft drinks that come in cans—and they taste metallic, too."

"I can look into it," Doug said. "Don't hold your breath, but it's an idea."

"Another idea is hotels. I was at that hotel in Chicago—" he shot a quick look at Martha, who was diligently doodling on her pad "—and all they had on the breakfast menu was the usual boring stuff. Prune juice. I mean, people ought to have a better choice of juice at breakfast, right? They're serving granola and yogurt at all the hotels now. Why not a hip fruit drink?"

"You're right," Doug said. "Why not?"

Blake glanced at Martha again. He wanted her to think he was right, too. Slowly, almost reluctantly, it seemed, she raised her eyes to him. And nodded.

He felt rewarded all out of proportion. She nodded! She liked his idea!

Buoyed, he gazed around the room. "Any other business?"

"Just the Christmas party," Helen said, glancing up from her laptop.

Blake wondered whether a holiday party was suitable for the agenda of a meeting of the company's top executives. Last year, everyone had talked about the party, which had wound up being a pasta-and-wine blowout in a private room at the Dockside Restaurant, down by the ferry pier. The planning had been casual and democratic, the way so much of the company's decisions were.

But this year was different. This year they were big. They'd had strong profits and were growing, and were going to have even stronger profits next year. "What do you think?" he asked Helen.

"It's been a landmark year. We've moved into the new headquarters, expanded... I think we ought to do something a little classier than last year."

"Okay." He could handle classy. "Martha, find out what we can budget for it."

"We're going to have to work fast," Penny spoke up. "It's pretty last minute. But—if we can afford it, and we do it on a Friday night instead of a Saturday, I can get us a small banquet room at the Tara."

"You're kidding!" Doug gave her an awestruck look. "The Tara? That's one of the fanciest hotels in town."

"I'm dating someone there," Penny explained. "I've got connections."

"I think we can afford it. I'll give you figures as soon as we're done here," Martha promised, then shot Blake a look. Her eyes were so dark. He recalled the way they'd glowed when they'd been sharing a pillow in Chicago. "Everyone deserves a fancy party at the Tara. It's been one heck of a year."

Blake believed it would be an even better year if he could get Martha to share a pillow with him again. But he thought about what the others in this room might think if they knew he'd been involved with her, and it brought him up short. In the old, casual days of the business, no one would have blinked. But now they had senior staff meetings. They planned Midwestern distribution and ritzy holiday parties. In a company with that kind of stature, the boss couldn't have sex with the senior financial officer—not unless they were engaged or married or something. Which Blake had no intention of becoming.

"I think we're done," he said, referring to the meeting. But maybe he meant he was done with Martha, even though he didn't want to be. He had to be. She was right about that.

Maybe he'd bring a date to the party. He didn't want that, either, but it might help him to survive the evening if he had someone else's legs to fixate on, someone else's eyes to distract him. What he felt for Martha was friendship, lust, admiration and grudging respect. If only he didn't respect her, he'd make another play for her, but she wanted his respect and he gave it.

No other woman interested him at the moment, but maybe he could find someone to stand by his side for the evening. Just to keep him sane.

If sanity was possible anymore.

9

"HOW DO I LOOK, Lucy?" Martha asked.

Lucy peered up from the knotted sock she'd been gnawing on. If she was startled to see Martha in an elegant black dress, she didn't reveal it. In fact, she didn't seem terribly impressed. The sock interested her more.

Martha didn't know what had gotten into her. The dress had been hanging in the front window of a boutique on Main Street, and it had called to her like an evil temptress, luring her in, commanding her to enter the store. She had prayed the dress would be the wrong size, but it wasn't. She'd tried it on, and it had fit as if it had been stitched directly onto her body. The shoulders, the bust, the waist, the gentle swirl of the skirt—it might as well have been custom-designed for her.

It was far too romantic a dress. But now that she was the chief financial officer of Blake's Fruit Brews, she supposed she ought to make a statement when she walked into the company party.

She didn't want to think about what statement she'd be making to Blake. Any statement she might make to him was irrelevant, anyway. They'd gone an entire month without exchanging anything more than business chat and perfunctory pleasantries. She had to admit she was impressed with his professional savvy.

At the newly instituted weekly senior staff meetings, he was always full of challenging ideas. When she'd first started working at the company last summer, he'd seemed laid-back to the point of passivity, but now he was on top of things, dynamic, innovative. Smart. She'd always known he was smart, but lately he'd made a point of demonstrating his intelligence at every opportunity.

So he was smart. He'd had to be, to get his company started in the first place. Martha had always had a soft spot in her heart for smart men, but that didn't mean she had a soft spot in her heart for Blake. Just because her pulse staggered when he entered a room, just because she felt looking into his eyes would endanger her mental health, just because every once in a while—more accurately, every single night—when she climbed into bed she remembered their lovemaking with an intensity that was almost unbearably painful.

It was a dream. Not what she wanted in her life. Nothing she could count on. Nothing that added up.

Still, there was no harm in looking good for the party. If she wanted, she could almost convince herself she looked great. Lucy's indifference didn't matter; she had no taste. Hadn't she fallen in love with Blake that October evening when he'd driven Martha home?

She donned her coat and grabbed her purse. "I'm on my way," she told Lucy, who wrestled the sock with great vigor, although it seemed to Martha that the sock was winning. "You've got water and food, and I expect you to behave yourself. I'll see you later."

The night was cold and crisp, the moonless sky sprayed with stars and the air so dry she could scarcely smell the ocean's scent as she drove north toward Main Street. The downtown shops were dressed in lights and tinsel: arches of silver garlands and plastic holly spanned the street. Yes, she thought, she looked damned good tonight. And she was going to have a fabulous time. She was going to shine. In the past seven weeks, she'd helped to land the Good Earth chain, gotten a promotion and a raise, slept with Blake without self-destructing, and almost gotten over her crush on him. She had done her Christmas shopping, decorated her house with scented red candles and pine boughs, and bought an extravagant dress.

Tonight, she was dressed to kill, and she was going to party.

BLAKE PREFERRED his bashes a little less tasteful, but considering how fast this one had been thrown together, and how little actual effort he'd had to contribute to it personally, he wasn't going to complain. The hotel had put them in a relatively small room, which made sense because they were a relatively small company, but there was plenty of space for a long buffet table, a freestanding bar, circular tables and chairs with candlelight centerpieces, a dance floor and a musical duo who managed to get a pretty full sound out of a guitar, an electronic keyboard and a drum synthesizer. Blake recognized the men—they played the resort circuit during the summers. Back in his bartending days, he used to listen to them perform at the hotel where he worked.

He was amazed that they'd been available to play tonight. Actually, he was amazed that Penny and Helen had thrown together the whole party. He supposed it had been possible because December was the off-season on Cape Cod. Hotels that had long waiting lists for available rooms between Memorial Day and Labor Day stood nearly empty during the winter months.

But even so, the Tara wasn't just a tourist motel on Route 28. It was a classy place, and Blake would have expected it to be booked. Obviously, it helped when your human resources director was dating a hotel manager during the party season.

He stood near the bar, hoping he didn't look as stiff as he felt in his charcoal-gray suit. He'd bought it yesterday, pleaded with the tailor to finish the alterations pronto, and cruised over to Filene's that morning to pick it up, along with the turquoise shirt and the silk tie he was wearing. He'd chosen the shirt because it didn't bore him. The tie was even less boring, a bright array of rainbow hues in an abstract pattern. He wasn't a necktie sort of guy, but now that he was a fruit juice company magnate, he imagined he was going to have to dress the part, at least sometimes.

He surveyed the dimly lit room and smiled. About thirty people had shown up so far; he expected at least thirty more. Many of his employees had brought spouses or dates. He'd considered bringing a date, too, but he'd thought of a million stupid reasons not to, plus one not-so-stupid reason: he didn't want to. Not after what had happened on his last date.

Martha hadn't arrived yet. It irked him that he was so keenly aware of her absence. When she finally came, she'd probably have some guy hanging off her arm. Probably someone perfect for her, a clean-cut, arrow-straight executive type who felt comfortable in suits and preferred not to have to spend the whole night with her, so if she ran off after an hour of sex he wouldn't mind.

If Blake had done as she'd asked and forgotten about the hour of sex he'd had with her, he wouldn't care if she brought a date with her. But he hadn't done as she'd asked—not for lack of trying. She was stuck under his skin like a splinter, a pinch of pain too deep to yank out.

"Hey, good-looking!" Sheila, one of the local plant managers, sidled up to him. He'd never seen her dolled up before, and she looked pretty good herself in a dress of clingy green velvet. She held a martini glass in one hand and a crab puff skewered on a toothpick in the other. "This is some party! I guess the company really is doing well, huh?"

"I guess it is," he said, wishing he could throw himself fully into a conversation with her. But his gaze scanned the room relentlessly, searching for someone who wasn't there, someone he wasn't supposed to care about.

Then he saw her, hovering just inside the door. It took him a full moment to register the fact that Martha could actually look so...lustrous. Not flashy, but suave and elegant in a black dress.

From where he stood, across the room from her, she seemed to glitter. Her eyes were bright, her lips rosy, her skin smooth and pale and her hair framing her face in shiny brown waves. Her shoes had small heels on them, just enough of a lift to make her look tall and to show off her slender ankles.

She happened to be standing right underneath a decorative sprig of mistletoe.

"Excuse me," Blake murmured to Sheila, giving her a friendly pat on the arm and then moving into the crowd, deftly avoiding collisions with the few couples dancing on the parquet floor as he wound a path toward the doorway. Blame it on the mistletoe, he thought. Blame it on Martha. He hadn't forgotten, and the way she looked tonight sure as hell wasn't going to help him forget anything, except maybe his common sense.

She didn't seem to notice him as he veered around one of the linen-covered tables and came up behind her. He tilted his head and stole a quick kiss on her cheek. Flinching, she spun around and gaped at him.

"The mistletoe," he explained, realizing that sounded pretty lame. He tried a winsome smile, hoping she wouldn't get all twisted in knots over a peck on the cheek.

She smiled back, hesitantly. Just the curve of her lips was enough to zap his entire nervous system. Her hair smelled like spring flowers. The scooped neckline of her dress showed off the creamy skin below her throat.

She looked breathtaking. Almost as wonderful as she'd looked completely naked. He tried to remember what his life had been like before he'd realized how alluring she was. He'd thought she was kind of plain, hadn't he? No one he would spot across a crowded room and feel compelled to kiss, with or without mistletoe.

He'd been himself back then, when he'd thought of her as nothing special. Life had been normal. Not anymore. But he didn't see a way back to that person he used to be—and standing beside Martha, gazing into her wide, dark eyes, he didn't care.

THIS WAS NOT supposed to happen.

She wasn't supposed to be kissed by Blake less than

a minute after she'd stepped through the doorway. People kissed people at office parties, she knew. Back at the firm where she'd worked in Boston, most of the kissing had occurred between upper-level management and young trainees, and the kissing generally hadn't started until everyone had taken one too many trips to the punch bowl.

To her great relief, she'd never been kissed by any of those well-lubricated fellows. It wasn't simply that she'd been a full-fledged accountant—she'd still been young enough for the wolves to view her as a tasty little lamb—but she suspected she'd had invisible rays emanating from her, warning lechers off. *Not interested!* her body language must have shouted. *Don't touch!*

Was she emanating different rays now?

She ought to tell Blake to back off, but for some reason she didn't want to. She wasn't herself tonight. She was dressed to the nines and feeling unusually confident. Let everyone admire her; let them think she looked stellar. Let Blake consider her irresistible. Why not? It was a party, and mistletoe was dangling from the ceiling above her head, and Blake wasn't a paunchy middle-aged Romeo trying to prove he still had what it took.

"This is really nice," she said, wandering farther into the room. A two-man band was set up in one corner, playing an old Beach Boys song. Waiters and waitresses carrying trays of hors d'oeuvres meandered through the room. A bartender mixed drinks in the corner opposite the band. Closing her eyes, Martha could imagine Blake a few years younger, tending bar at a similar party.

He wouldn't have looked so handsome then, she decided. A younger Blake wouldn't have had intriguing laugh lines fanning out from the corners of his eyes. His dimples wouldn't be quite so deeply etched. And he wouldn't have been able to carry off an outfit like the one he was wearing tonight—a shirt that echoed the astonishing blue of his eyes, a tie that looked like a painter's tantrum, and a suit that fit perfectly, emphasizing his broad shoulders, his trim hips and the length of his legs.

As they strolled deeper into the room together, she realized it was more than just his appearance that made him so much more attractive to her than he'd been last summer, when she'd first entered his office clutching the classified ad from the *Cape Cod Times* and been dazzled by his sunny good looks. Every Monday since returning from Chicago, she'd sat in staff meetings with him and listened to him fire off ideas, suggestions, goals for the company. She knew he didn't have the kind of business education she and Doug and some of the others at the meetings had—in fact, he'd hired people like her and Doug to make up for his lack of expertise.

But he seemed more dynamic now, more purposeful, more on top of things, not merely the creative force behind an innovative product but someone who could visualize a future for his company. When she'd first met him, he'd seemed like a gorgeous hunk with good instincts and more than his share of luck. Now he seemed like a man who was in charge and knew it.

He escorted her to the bar. "What would you like to drink?" he asked.

"Wine," she said, smiling at the bartender. "A chardonnay, please." She remembered the wine she and

Blake had had at dinner at Marta's, that odd little basement café in Chicago. She hadn't known what kind of wine they'd been drinking, and it hadn't mattered. What had mattered was that it was delicious—and that Blake had lifted his glass in a toast to her.

She glanced up at him, wondering if he still remembered that night. Probably not. She'd told him to forget it. He'd probably drunk toasts to a dozen other women since then.

But he was standing beside her now, all but ignoring the many other women in the room. Gone was his flirty smile, his carefree manner. When one of the administrative assistants from the marketing department edged up next to him and sent him an inviting grin, he merely greeted her with a nod and turned back to Martha in time to hand her her wine.

It was almost as if he were announcing, in front of the entire staff of Blake's Fruit Brews, that he was with Martha tonight.

Silly thought. He wasn't with her. They'd had a fling, and it was over, and she was confusing fantasy and reality again if she thought Blake was actually displaying a particular attentiveness toward her. He had probably greeted every woman with a mistletoe kiss upon her arrival, and ushered each of them to the bar for a drink.

"I like your dress," he remarked as they moved away from the bar.

"Thank you." He'd probably complimented every other woman's outfit, too.

"Do you want to eat, or do you want to dance?" he asked.

She laughed. "Are those my only two choices?"

"I could suggest some other possibilities, but you'd

probably slap me in the face if I mentioned them," he murmured, grinning mischievously.

Well, all right. He hadn't forgotten Chicago. And fool that she was, she was secretly pleased. "I wouldn't slap your face, Blake," she assured him. "I'm not a violent person."

"Then let's dance." He took her glass and placed it, along with his own, on an empty table. Then he settled his right hand at the small of her back, enveloped her right hand in his left, and drew her out onto the parquet floor at the center of the room.

The duo was playing an Eagles song, slow and plaintive. Other people were paired up on the dance floor, so Martha wasn't all alone with Blake. She tried to pretend that dancing with him meant nothing, that she felt nothing in his arms. She tried to pretend that this was just a dance—as the official host of the company party he would be dancing with all the other women, too—and that if his thumb just happened to be moving alluringly against her waist, it wasn't a conscious act on his part. She tried to pretend his spicy scent didn't warm her from the inside out, and the firm contours of his chest didn't make her want to turn back the clock a month, to a night she'd run her hands and her lips over his bare chest, a night she'd been even closer to him than she was now.

Turning back the clock had been simple enough when daylight saving time had ended. Why couldn't she turn it back in her mind tonight? Just for this one night, a Christmas gift to herself, just for as long as the party lasted.

"I've got to tell you, Martha," he murmured, his voice floating through her hair to reach her ear, "that I haven't forgotten."

Had he been reading her mind? Or had he simply been as tortured by memories as she? It was hard to cling to her rationality when he was holding her so tightly, dancing so slowly with her. "I had good reasons for telling you to forget," she reminded him, her voice low and throaty. His nearness seemed to have affected her ability to breathe. Her lungs seemed out of sync with her heartbeat. Her feet barely moved on the polished wood floor.

"I remember your reasons," he said, moving his thumb against the small of her back again, as if to make sure she knew it was a deliberate gesture. "I even remember thinking they were good reasons. But I still haven't forgotten."

"Oh." She swallowed. He tucked her hand between their bodies, drawing her closer to himself. "Everyone can see us," she whispered, wondering if everyone could also see her blushing. She was sure she was; her cheeks were burning.

"What do they see? Two people dancing?"

Maybe they saw one person dancing and the other feeling like a nerdy high school student on the day of the prom, wondering how she'd wound up on the dance floor with the class Adonis. Maybe they saw Blake enjoying a dance and Martha drifting into a dream that seemed more real than reality.

"If you don't want to dance with me, just say so," he said.

She wanted to dance with him. She wanted to stand within his embrace, savoring his height, his physique, the heat of him. She wanted to feel the music swirl around them, soft and seductive, and know that the class Adonis was unashamed to be seen on the dance floor with her. Not just unashamed—he seemed almost proud to have her in his arms. Proud and extremely sure of himself.

"This is fine," she managed to reply.

She decided there would be no harm in enjoying being in Blake's arms again for the duration of the song. Once it ended, she would thank Blake for the dance and release him so he could ask someone else for the next dance. But when the music ended, he didn't abandon her. Her "thank you" remained unspoken, lingering on her tongue as he escorted her back to the table where he'd left their drinks. He pulled out a chair for her, then sat facing her, gazing intently at her. "What do you think of this?" he asked, indicating the room with a wave of his hand.

"The party, you mean?" At his nod, she answered, "It's fancier than I expected."

"You dressed for a fancy party," he noted.

"Yes, well...that was a touch of madness on my part."

"Madness?" He chuckled and sipped his drink. "It's a great dress."

"Thank you."

"You would have looked out of place if you'd worn it to a party that wasn't this fancy."

She conceded with a smile and a nod.

"Maybe," he continued, mirroring her smile, "you knew deep in your subconscious or something that the party was going to be like this. Maybe your thoughts were headed in the same direction as mine, all along."

Meaning what? She and Blake were actually thinking alike? Not only had he been behaving like a true leader at the staff meetings, laying out ideas, delegating authority, making demands and pushing the company, rather than letting it pull him along. But when it came to the company party, he'd authorized a gala that was what Martha had intuitively known it would be.

This was dangerous. It was bad enough that he starred in all her fantasies. Even worse was that she *liked* him. She'd liked him in Chicago, and she'd tried to ignore that, but over the past few weeks, she'd only grown to like him more.

And there they were at his company's Christmas party, and he was dancing with her and sitting with her, proclaiming to all his colleagues that he and Martha were...what? Friends? Intimates? Martha was afraid to guess.

"The thing is, Martha..." The band launched into a bouncy rendition of "Bad, Bad Leroy Brown." The song was greeted with good-natured groans, but a large group of people swarmed onto the dance floor to boogie to the lively tune. Blake ignored them, his attention fully on her. "I've been feeling real bad since Chicago," he said.

Regret, she figured. Disappointment. Maybe disgust with himself, with them both, for having lost control as they had.

"The company's going great guns, I like what's happening there—but I just feel, I don't know. Incomplete. At loose ends. Like something's missing." He reached across the table to take her hand. "I really tried to forget, but I can't. I don't want to. I think—" he swallowed, his gaze so earnest she sighed "—what happened in Chicago was too good to forget. I think you ran away, and you're still running away and it's silly. I think you should stop running."

She hadn't expected such blunt honesty. Blake had never seemed particularly dishonest to her, but still...

There was more than honesty in his declaration. There was a challenge. He was daring her to stop running away, to accept the possibility, outlandish though it seemed, that maybe her dream had come true, the fantasy merging with the reality. Maybe it was time for her to admit that Blake was more than just a gorgeous, virile creature designed to stoke the fires of her imagination. He was a smart, ambitious, open-minded man. He had made love to her with power and tenderness. He had shared his thoughts with her, his ideas and feelings.

And oh, yes, he was honest.

"All right," she whispered, rotating her hand to weave her fingers through his. "Let's stop trying to forget."

SHE WASN'T REALLY sure how the rest of the party went. She knew she had a splendid time, laughing and dancing, nibbling on tasty tidbits from the buffet table and the waiters' trays, joking with Doug and discussing lipstick with Helen when they'd run into each other in the ladies' room. Details of the evening blurred together, but her overall mood was elation. Trying to forget what her heart, her mind and her soul steadfastly insisted could not be forgotten had taken its toll on her. Now she was free to remember, to acknowledge the reality of it.

She didn't spend the entire party by Blake's side, but that didn't matter. Even when he was chatting with some of his sales staff at one end of the room and she was evaluating the miniquiches with Pete from quality control at the other, she never lost her certainty

that she and Blake were still together, inextricably
linked. Maybe the link was a shared memory.

Maybe it was something more.

Martha didn't care what it was. All she knew was
that it made her feel beautiful and confident, brave
and beloved.

By eleven-thirty, the crowd had thinned out consid-
erably. The band packed its instruments and the room
filled with the aroma of strong coffee. With smooth
discretion, the hotel was letting the guests know the
party was over.

But she wasn't going to run away. Not this time.

Blake was conferring with the musicians, shaking
their hands and thanking them. Then he turned, spotted Martha and crossed the room to her. "Are you
leaving?" he asked, touching her shoulder, a gesture
both casual and proprietary.

She peered into his eyes, hoping to find her answer
there. Unable to read a clear response in the startling
blue irises, she shrugged. "The party's ending, so..."

"Don't leave," he whispered, sending her a secret
smile before he released her shoulder and moved toward the door to say good-night to a few other guests
about to depart.

She stood where she was, anticipation and anxiety
warring within her. She was under no obligation to
obey him. But if she stayed, it would be not because
he'd asked her but because she wanted to.

She wanted to. Even if she had no idea what would
happen next. Even if she did have an idea what would
happen eventually, not in the next hour but in a while,
in time, and that idea wasn't a happy one. She wanted
to stay, anyway.

More people trickled out the door. A few of them

said goodbye to both her and Blake, as if they were a publicly acknowledged couple cohosting the affair. As busboys swept in to clear the sparse leftovers from the buffet, Blake tucked Martha's hand around his elbow and strolled with her out of the room.

She accompanied him without asking where they were going or what they'd be doing. In Chicago, she'd known exactly where she'd been going with Blake in that hotel, but now it didn't matter. She could as easily envision herself sitting in a coffee bar with him for half the night, discussing holiday movies, as going to bed with him.

"I've got to go settle the account," he told her, crossing the hotel's lobby to the desk. The night clerk led him into a back office and presented him with a bill. "Can we afford it?" he asked, grinning and handing the invoice to Martha.

She skimmed it, then studied it more closely. The bar tab wasn't as big as she'd expected, which meant the hotel had probably billed everything fairly. She added the column of numbers in her head and nodded. "It looks about right," she said.

"Okay." He handed the clerk his corporate credit card, then added, as she turned to leave the office with the bill, "Do you have any rooms available tonight?"

She hesitated in the doorway. "I believe so. Do you want me to add it to your bill?"

"No. The party is being paid for by the company. The room is personal." He handed the clerk another credit card, then waited until she left the office before he turned to Martha. "Okay?" he asked.

She could have scolded him for his presumptuousness. She could have reverted to her old self and run for cover. But once again she was stunned by his honesty, this time expressed not in words but in the sheer force of his gaze as he studied her. She saw not just honesty but raw desire and something more, something she would have called love if she'd been fantasizing.

She could accept that his desire was real, as real as hers for him. She wouldn't deceive herself about anything more, but she wouldn't flee, either. She would accept the truth, whatever it was.

"Okay," she said.

Five minutes later, the clerk returned to the office with a room key. She eyed the two of them in their party apparel, Martha's evening purse the closest thing either of them had to luggage, and asked, rather unnecessarily, "Will you be needing a bellhop?"

"I don't think so," Blake said, taking the key in one hand and Martha's hand in the other. They left the office, Martha feeling slightly embarrassed and terribly naughty and deciding that what the clerk thought was irrelevant.

The room was clean and cozy, its window overlooking the pool patio, which was vacant and dimly lit. Martha turned from the view as Blake locked the door. He walked across the room, his footsteps silent on the carpet. Her pulse drummed in her ears and she had to exert herself to stand still, not to run from him—or hurl herself at him.

They were going to do it right this time. No worry about whether this was a gift, whether she could allow herself only an hour, whether Blake was suitable for her, whether he cared enough about her, whether she would wake up tomorrow and find herself alone, aching, her sheets rumpled around her. No worry about whether he was her dream man. He wasn't. He was real, flesh and bone, passion and need.

He reached her, stood before her, lifted his hand to her cheek and dug his fingers into her hair. Slowly, so slowly she nearly wept with impatience, he lowered his mouth to hers. His kiss was soft, leisurely, a warning that he had no intention of rushing. Whatever occurred between them tonight was going to take longer than an hour.

She slid her hands up along the sleeves of his jacket. No padding shaped the jacket; all she felt was Blake, rugged shoulders, muscle and sinew. Struggling to match his restraint, she brushed her lips against his and kept her hands where they were, resisting the urge to yank open his tie—and his shirt and his trousers.

"This feels so good," he whispered, twirling his fingers lazily through her hair and touching his mouth to hers again. His lips were warm, carrying a hint of the coffee he'd drunk as the party had wound down. Only after he'd kissed her like that, gently, almost chastely, for several minutes, did he allow his tongue to venture out and trace the seal of her lips.

A hot shiver skimmed down her spine to her hips. She wanted him, now. She wanted him more than she'd ever known she could want a man.

"Blake, I never..."

He pulled his mouth from hers, lifted her hair and pressed a kiss against the side of her neck, under her ear. She sighed, feeling another surge of heat course down her back, making her hips so heavy her legs swayed beneath her.

"You never what?"

"Never felt what I feel with you."

"That's because I'm me," he said simply. It wasn't a boast, simply a statement of his uniqueness.

She smiled. "No. I mean—" she sighed again as he grazed down her neck to her throat "—I'm not a very sensual person."

He leaned back and laughed. "Oh, yeah," he said sarcastically. "I noticed."

"I mean it, Blake. I'm not very—well, I don't date much. I don't get carried away by things. I'm an accountant. By the numbers, by the book."

"Well, this book is erotic," he murmured. "And you've sure got my number." With that, he swept her into his arms, his self-control evidently gone. He raised his head and covered her lips with his in a hot, hard, devouring kiss. His tongue claimed her and his fingers fisted in her hair, holding her head steady as he plundered her mouth. She wanted to whimper, to groan in relief.

She heard the whisper of her zipper being opened down her back, exposing it to a wedge of cool air. She groped for his tie, tugged the knot loose, and tore at the buttons of his shirt. Without breaking the kiss, he chuckled. Her mouth filled with his laughter.

"Don't tell me you think this is funny," she warned, still not sure he hadn't meant that comment as an insult the last time they'd been together like this.

"I think *you're* funny," he explained. "Telling me you aren't sensual."

"I'm not," she argued. "I just want you to take your shirt off."

"Hmm. Just my shirt? I guess you're not that sensual, after all."

"Well..." She was forced to laugh, too. She decided laughing was appropriate. Maybe all this passion burning between her and Blake was funny, in its own way. "I think I want more than just your shirt off."

"Ah." He opened the last button of his shirt and removed it and his jacket in one graceful motion. His hand fell to the buckle of his belt. "You want this off, too?"

She could feel herself blushing. "Yes," she admitted shyly.

"Sounds kind of sensual." He slipped the belt through the buckle. "Anything more?" he asked.

Her cheeks were so hot she could almost hear them sizzle. "Blake..."

"Maybe you're sensual enough to want my fly open, too," he suggested, grinning darkly. He inched the zipper down. She glimpsed dark silk underneath. He hooked his thumbs over the waistband of the slacks and struck an indolent pose. "Anything else?" he asked.

"Yes." She barely heard her own voice, but the sight of his glorious chest, his flat abdomen and that open fly mesmerized her.

"I'd say, for a by-the-book accountant, you're a hell of a lot more sensual than you know." He edged his trousers down, catching the elastic waist of his boxers and pulling them down, as well. Uninhibited. Shameless. Unabashedly aroused. "I'll leave my socks on," he offered, kicking away his trousers once they dropped to the floor. "I don't want to shock you."

She laughed again, although she was having a little trouble breathing. "Take your socks off, too," she said, feeling both overwhelmed by him and also oddly powerful. No man had ever stripped for her. She couldn't imagine ever wanting one to—until now. Until Blake.

"You sure? I don't want to embarrass you," he taunted.

"I'm sure. No socks."

"Well, if you insist." He planted one hand on her shoulder for balance, then lifted each foot in turn and plucked off the socks. "There," he said, standing naked before her. "Feeling sensual yet?"

"Yes." She was feeling light-headed, too. Her heart was beating too fast. Her body seemed molten, her thigh muscles taut and her breasts aching. Her hands craved the feel of him, the satiny heat of his skin, the hard length of him announcing how much he needed her. She was feeling very, very sensual.

He turned her around and finished unzipping her dress, chasing the zipper down her back with a string of kisses. He paused to flick open the clasp of her bra, then continued down, peeling the dress off her arms until it hung limp at her waist. Then he pulled her backward until they reached the bed. He sat, caught her between his legs and eased the dress, her slip and her panty hose down her legs all at once.

When at last she was as naked as he was, he pulled her into his lap. His kiss was deep, possessive, aggressive. She didn't care. At last she could touch him, stroke him, let her hands roam across his sleekly muscled body. She could rake her fingernails down through the golden hair on his legs. She could nip his shoulder, lick his nipples, let her hair rain across his chest. She could be as sensual as he presumed she was.

He caressed her with equal enthusiasm, using his hands, his mouth, his body. He rubbed her insteps with his toes, nudged her thighs apart with his knees, pressed her against him so her breasts felt the friction of the hair on his chest. He stroked his fingers between her legs, sliding deep into her, making her feel empty, tender, desperate for him to fill her. Her body seemed to reach for him, plead for him to take her, make her his, offer her the ultimate proof of her own sensuality.

And he did. With a fierce, conquering thrust he taught her everything her body had always known, buried somewhere under the numbers and the books, under the professionalism and the reticence. With each plunging motion he taught her she was beautiful, desirable, utterly feminine. He taught her she was immeasurably sensual, and when at last her body erupted in lush pulses of pleasure, he taught her that she was his.

10

BLAKE SMILED. A sliver of morning light wedged through the space where the drapes didn't quite meet, the alarm clock on the night table read seven-fifteen, and Martha was still with him.

She had her back to him, her head cushioned by his upper arm. Her bottom curved against his groin, but she was sleeping too soundly to notice the effect she was having on him.

He wouldn't wake her up. She was probably exhausted, given the way the night had gone. He ought to be exhausted, too, and he was, physically. Mentally, he was wide-awake.

This situation could turn out to be pretty damned terrific, he thought. No more hang-ups or complications, no more avoiding, no more ignoring, no more panic or pretending. Just Martha and him, a good friendship and great sex. Not a bad way to ring in the holidays.

If he hadn't gotten to know Martha, he doubted he would have asked for Santa to leave someone like her under his tree. But sometimes the best present you got was the surprise in the mysterious box, the gift you weren't expecting, the one you didn't even know you wanted.

And on the subject of Christmas presents, he supposed he ought to buy one for Martha. He wondered what she would like. He'd never been inside her house, so he didn't know if she was the crystal-figurine-and-porcelain type or the scented-candle-and-earthenware type. Flowers? Clichéd, plus after a few days they'd shrivel and die. Besides, Blake believed flowers were appropriate on only three occasions: to mark a special date, like an anniversary or a birthday; to seduce a woman you hadn't gotten into bed yet; or to apologize. Blake didn't know Martha's birthday, they weren't celebrating any anniversaries and he'd already gotten her into bed. And he hadn't done anything to apologize for.

Jewelry? No way. Too many serious implications.

Perfume? He leaned forward and inhaled the scent of her shampoo, then dipped his head to sniff her neck. She smelled like herself, warm and clean, the faintest hint of a soap fragrance on her skin. He'd never noticed her wearing perfume, and that suited him fine. He would rather smell a woman's own scent than something artificial.

Damn. He really needed to figure out something to give her. A scarf? Too generic. A sweater? Too personal. A book? He didn't know what she read. A board game? A water bottle for her bicycle? A gadget for her kitchen? A toy for her dog?

It should have troubled him that he didn't know her well enough to choose a gift for her. But he felt as if he knew everything he needed to know about her. He knew what made her feel good, and what made her feel great, and what made her feel out of this world. He knew that if he touched her here she'd stop breathing, and if he kissed her there she'd moan. He knew that he would trust her with his life and—he hoped—she would trust him with hers. The rest was just details, as far as he was concerned.

Her hips shifted, pressing more firmly against him. He was already hard, but her unconscious movements made him harder. He slid his hand down her side and forward, through the downy hair below her belly to the soft, damp cleft between her legs.

She gasped. He leaned around her and saw her eyes flutter open. "Blake?" she whispered.

"Were you expecting someone else?"

Smiling sleepily, she reached for his hand but didn't pull him away. Instead she rolled onto her back and peered up at him, drowsy and dazed. He strummed his fingers against her and she gasped again.

He liked her best this way, defenseless, all her self-protective armor gone. He'd goaded her into defense-lessness last night with his playful striptease, and she was still here with him, uninhibited. She'd learned how to laugh, how to enjoy emotionally what she obviously enjoyed physically.

This was how he wanted her: stripped down to her essence and completely vulnerable to him.

Still stroking her, he lowered his mouth to her breast. It was small but firm, the skin soft and warm, her nipple a tight little nub that grew stiffer with each flick of his tongue. He kissed her other breast, loving the way her entire body responded to each kiss, each caress. Her back arched, her hands gripped his shoulders, and she grew hotter and wetter with each brush of his fingers.

If she had run away last night the way she had in Chicago, they wouldn't have had this morning together. He would have awakened alone and horny, and she wouldn't have been naked and aroused in his arms, sighing and writhing and wanting him as much as he wanted her.

He kissed lower. Her skin tasted slightly sweet, slightly salty. Her rib cage was narrow, her waist narrower. Her belly was smooth. It rose and fell with her breathing, a strange, ragged rhythm.

He moved lower yet. He didn't know what to give her for Christmas, but he could give her this right now, and she would love it.

At the first touch of his mouth she groaned. He used his lips and tongue; he ran his hands gently along her inner thighs, holding her open for him. He felt her tensing, her body resisting, fighting the inevitable and then yielding to the ultimate sensation. Her broken cry turned him on even more.

He slid up along her body and plunged into her, needing to feel her clenching around him, needing her to come while he was inside her. It didn't take much, and thank heaven, because he didn't have much in him. Just a few deep, strong thrusts and she was there, and he was with her, riding the same waves, carried away by the same tide.

He clung to her, too weary to let go. With his last scrap of energy he rolled onto his side, bringing her with him. She nestled against him, breathing hard, her hand flat against his chest, against his pounding heart. After several long minutes, he heard her murmur, "Oh, my."

"You liked that?" he asked, smoothing down her hair with his hand.

"Yes."

"Was this the first time for you?"

"Well, actually..." She paused, ruminating. He wondered what she had to think over. Either she'd made love that way before or she hadn't. He kind of hoped she hadn't—a male ego thing, wanting to be her first—but when her silence continued, he eased back to look at her. Why couldn't she answer? Was she afraid he'd think less of her if she'd had some previous experience?

"I'm not sure," she finally admitted.

"You're not sure?" He almost laughed. How could a woman not be sure about something like that? "What, did you sleep through it or something?"

"I think so, yes," she said somberly.

"Then the guy must not have been very good."

"Oh, he was—" Again she hesitated. "He wasn't as good as you," she finally said. It didn't sound as if she was struggling to compliment him, though. It sounded as if she was simply stating a basic truth.

He accepted it that way; earning her praise wasn't as important as figuring out what she was getting at. "I wasn't asking you to compare, Martha. I was just wondering—I mean, when you and I make love, I can't imagine either of us sleeping through it."

"Neither can I," she said, giving him a shy smile, so sweet it touched his heart. "That was completely different. When I'm with you...it's like nothing I've ever known before."

She was still smiling, her eyes dark yet glittering, reminding him of the dark sparkle of her dress last night, the dark sparkle of her spirit. He liked her smile. He wanted to keep looking at it for the rest of the morning. He couldn't quite read it, but it intrigued him.

"I love you, Blake," she said.

So that was what her smile meant: *love*. A bolt of fear shot through him.

He considered his reply carefully. Very carefully. What he'd thought of as friendship and great sex—magnificent sex, extraordinary sex—she was defining as love. Love had never crossed his mind. Love was a whole other thing. Love meant commitments and obligations and being able to give exactly what your woman wanted for Christmas because you knew her so well.

He didn't know Martha so well. The truth was, he wasn't sure he wanted to. He'd been perfectly content to leave things at the level of friendship and sex.

He had to respond, but he wasn't sure what to say. He would do anything in the world not to hurt Martha's feelings—anything but lie to her. Lying was as distasteful to him as spending the past few weeks pretending he'd forgotten what they'd shared in Chicago.

But he didn't want to hurt her. God, he didn't want that.

His failure to speak was hurting her. He could tell. Her beautiful, enigmatic smile faded, melting away like ice on the sidewalk under an August sun. "We have something special here, Martha," he said, knowing as soon as the words were out that they were pitifully inadequate.

"All right." Her smile was only a shadow now. She withdrew from his arms and sat up. "I'm sorry."

"No." He was the one who ought to be apologizing.

"I shouldn't have said anything. Forget it. I just..." Her voice cracked, and she ducked, eluding his hand when he reached out to pull her back. "I thought we could be honest with each other, that's all."

"We can be. We are." He'd been as honest as she had. Unfortunately, his honest reaction wasn't the one she'd been hoping for. He knew it, and she knew it.

"Don't run away," he pleaded. But this time, she wasn't really running. She'd stated her terms, and by saying nothing he'd pretty much stated his, and she was rejecting his.

He could think of ways to turn the situation around. He could imply that love might lie in their future, that she ought to give him a chance, that she ought to relax and enjoy what they had, and let things develop in their own time.

However, he knew that if he said that, what he'd mean would be letting things develop in *his* time. And his time might be forever. He simply couldn't imagine declaring his love and promising eternity to any woman. Certainly not to Martha, who despite her passion and all her other attractive qualities, had never been the kind of woman he could see himself actually loving and promising eternity.

She was an accountant, for heaven's sake.

He watched glumly as she padded barefoot across the room to gather her clothing. She had a beautiful back, slim and lithe. He'd kissed every square inch of that back last night, and he'd loved it. Could he stretch that notion to encompass the possibility that he loved *her*?

No. He loved having sex with her. He loved sleeping with her cuddled up next to him. He loved waking at around three in the morning and making love with her again, and then talking in the dark, whispering from pillow to pillow. She'd told him she was going to spend Christmas with her sister's family at their parents' house in Connecticut, and he'd told her he'd be heading up the Cape to his parents' place in Yarmouthport. They'd talked about whether they would get snow before the new year, and she'd described her dog's adoration of snow. "I throw Lucy snowballs and she catches them in her mouth and eats them, and she's so excited," Martha had told him. He'd remembered his own dog's love of snow as a puppy, and the dog's gradual impatience with it as he grew old. Blake had wondered aloud whether he would grow sick of snow when he himself grew old, and Martha had laughed and said she couldn't imagine Blake ever being too old to love snow.

It had been a wonderful night, arguably one of the best nights of his life. But that didn't mean he loved Martha.

He didn't want her to leave, but he'd forfeited the right to stop her. He continued to watch as she collected the rest of her clothing and carried it to the bathroom, closing the door quietly behind her. After a minute, he heard the hiss of the shower running.

He could sneak into the bathroom and join her in the shower. They could run the soap over each other's bodies. He could make her come again, with the water spilling over her, rushing across her skin and making her slick. He could do all sorts of wild things with her, things that might make her want to return to his bed.

But he wouldn't. If he did she would hate him, and the only thing worse than having her love him would be having her hate him. Even if he didn't join her in the shower, she probably hated him. By the time she was done drying off and getting dressed, she'd likely hate him with all her heart—and he knew she had an incredible heart.

Once again, he thought of what he could do to salvage the morning. Once again, he came up empty. He'd lost her, and the only way to win her back would be to tell her he loved her. Which was a lie.

The kindest thing—the *only* thing—he could do was remain in bed and let Martha walk away. It wasn't his choice, but it was really the only fair thing to do.

"I BLEW IT," she said disconsolately.

She and her sister had taken over their mother's kitchen to do the postdinner cleanup. The room was redolent with the aroma of the turkey the family had just devoured. Her parents were in the den watching Nancy's children play with their new Christmas toys, while Nancy's husband had generously volunteered to take Lucy for a long walk in the bitter-cold evening.

"Telling a guy you love him isn't always a mistake," Nancy argued, passing a wine goblet to Martha to dry. She was three years older than Martha, but she rarely gave Martha advice because they were so different. Nancy had always been gregarious and artistic and given to large, romantic gestures.

"In this case," Martha argued, "telling him was a mistake."

"It hurt you because he didn't say he loved you, too. But at least you got everything out in the open. You found out where he stood—and where he stands is Stinko-ville. He's a jerk. Not the only jerk in the world, just the jerk du jour. He doesn't deserve you, Martha. You're better off without him."

"He's my boss," Martha reminded her sister.

Nancy sighed. She looked like a slightly larger version of Martha, a bit taller, a bit broader in the shoulder and hip, her face a bit rounder and prettier. Passing Martha another wineglass to dry, she said, "I know all that stuff about office ethics. But do you really think he's going to fire you for blurting out that you're in love with him?"

"No." Martha sighed as well, a sigh torn from a bleak, wounded place in her soul. She silently acknowledged that she'd be feeling just as dreadful even if she hadn't admitted her feelings to Blake. She might have been able to delude herself for a little longer that he returned her love, but prolonging a delusion wouldn't have been a good thing in the end. As Nancy had pointed out, it was better to have gotten her feelings out in the open and found out that he didn't share them, so she could plan what to do, how to mend her heart, how to get over him and get on with her life.

"Listen to me," Nancy said, shaking the excess water from the final wineglass. "I was in love a million times before I met Larry. You fall in love, you fall out of love. You hurt, then you heal. And you can take the pain and do something creative with it."

Easy for her to say, Martha thought miserably. Nancy was a creative person. In Martha's world, too much creativity usually wound up winning an accountant jail time.

"I'm not creative."

"Sure you are. Everyone is." The last glass delivered safely into Martha's hands, Nancy lifted a scouring pad and attacked a roasting pan. "Have you finished decorating your house? Now's a good time. Sew some drapes. Paint the bathroom bright red. Bake a cake. Try needlepoint. Do something crazy."

"I'm going to quit my job," Martha said.

Nancy gaped at her. "What are you, crazy?"

Martha shook her head. Quitting her job would be the least crazy thing she'd done since she had that ridiculously erotic dream back in October. She'd been mulling over the idea of leaving Blake's Fruit Brews ever since she'd walked out of the Tara Hotel with nothing but a broken heart and tattered pride. Throughout the final week and a half of work before the holiday, she'd contemplated the possibility of resigning. She had grown to love working at Blake's Brews, and she wondered whether quitting was a way of punishing herself for her stupidity in falling in love with Blake—and her even greater stupidity in putting him in the awkward position of having to admit, through his silence, that he didn't love her.

But she knew she wouldn't be leaving the job to punish herself. She'd do it to preserve her dignity. She didn't see how she could continue to work for Blake after making love with him, spending the night with him...opening her heart to him.

"It's my New Year's resolution," she told her sister, who had resumed scouring the roasting pan with unnecessary vigor. "It hurts too much to stay there. It's too embarrassing."

"Why are you embarrassed? Everyone makes mistakes."

"Everyone doesn't sleep with the boss and tell him she loves him."

Nancy cursed under her breath. "Your problem, Martha, is that you always have to do everything by the book. Everything has to balance. You can't fudge a calculation."

"I miscalculated this time. Critically."

"All right. So why can't you forgive yourself?"

"I can forgive myself," Martha insisted. "In fact, I'll even give some thought to painting the bathroom— not red, of course, but maybe a nice soft blue." The color of Blake's eyes, she thought dolefully, and sighed. "I just don't see how I can work for him anymore. I've got my sanity to think of." Her sanity had been questionable ever since that October evening when Blake had driven her home and told her about the gift of an hour that would be waiting for her later that night. Obviously there was a connection between him and her mental stability. She had to put some distance between him and herself in order to become sane again.

If she left Blake's Fruit Brews, she would have no more erotic dreams of a mysterious man who could have been Blake's clone barging into her bedroom and making love to her. She would relinquish her memories of the real Blake making love to her with just as much intensity, just as much rapture. She would recover. She would get her old mind back, a mind that knew the difference between fantasy and reality and didn't fall madly in love with big, blond hunks who were inappropriate for her.

"Don't do anything rash," Nancy cautioned. "It's a good job, you've gotten a promotion, you've bought a house—"

"I'm finished doing rash things," Martha promised her sister. "Quitting wouldn't be rash. It would be sensible. And I'll find another job. Or I'll sell the house. Don't worry about me."

Nancy turned back to her, then wrapped her in a crushing hug. Martha felt warm water from Nancy's hands seep through her sweater, but she didn't mind. She loved her sister, and she needed a hug. "Don't tell me not to worry," Nancy murmured. "If I want to worry, I will. Just promise me you won't fall in love with someone you work for, ever again."

"Ah, so you agree it was a stupid thing to do."

Nancy snorted and released Martha. "Of course it was stupid. But so what? Most people know how to make the most of doing something stupid. That's your problem, Martha. You don't know how to enjoy something that goes against the rules and makes no sense.''

Martha didn't argue, but she knew her sister was wrong. If Martha had learned anything, it was that she actually enjoyed breaking the rules and doing things that made no sense. And that was almost as scary as the understanding that she'd fallen in love with a man who didn't—and never would—love her.

"IT'S A JOKE, isn't it?'' Doug stood in the doorway of her office, staring at her. "You aren't really leaving, are you?''

Martha glanced up from her computer screen and smiled faintly. "No joke, Doug. I handed in my resignation.''

"Why?''

She couldn't very well tell him. It was hard enough entering the building on the first workday of the new year. Even harder typing a brief resignation letter and walking it down the hall to Penny in human resources. Harder yet searching the hall for a hiding place when she heard Blake's voice—she'd shut herself in the supply closet and felt like the world's biggest coward, but better that than to have to face him, to let him see how miserable she was, to let him witness her humiliation. The savvy number cruncher, who was at heart just a moonstruck girl with an unrequited crush, was allowed to hide in a supply room if it would protect her pea-size ego.

But she wasn't going to explain all that to Doug. "Personal reasons," she said, hoping he had enough tact not to question her further.

He did—but her answer clearly didn't satisfy him.

He marched into her office, looking around as if searching for evidence that she was serious about leaving. She hadn't started packing her things yet, of course. In her letter of resignation, she'd offered to stay on a full month or until a replacement was found, whichever happened first. She would have preferred to depart immediately, but she was a professional and knew the proper way to do things. In the meantime, she'd continue to draw her salary, which wasn't a bad thing.

"Do you have another job lined up?" Doug asked, dropping onto the visitor's chair alongside Martha's desk. "Something better than this? Nah, nothing could be better than this."

In terms of the job itself, he was right. She couldn't imagine finding a job with a company as easy and flexible as Blake's Brews, a company in which the employees had so much input into the way the place was run, right down to the arrangement of the pool table and the dartboard in the lounge.

"I haven't found anything yet," she confessed. A pen lay on her blotter, tempting her. She folded her hands in her lap to keep from fidgeting with the pen. She didn't want Doug to know how tense she was.

"Have you started looking?"

"The new year just began," she pointed out. "Businesses are just beginning to get back into the rhythm of things. I'll start looking soon. Or I might hang out a shingle and open a private practice." She'd begun considering that possibility after she'd returned from Connecticut. On a long, blustery walk along the beach with Lucy, she'd chewed it over. She didn't have much in the way of savings, having sunk a lot of money into her house, so it would be hard to tide herself over while she tried to build a clientele. The timing was bad, too; to capitalize on the tax season, she would have had to start soliciting clients last fall—before the dream man had visited her and turned her universe upside down.

She'd tried the notion out on Lucy, who had actually stopped chasing a seagull to bark her approval. Of course, if Martha was accepting career counseling from her dog, it didn't bode well for her sanity.

"Why?" Doug repeated. "Don't you like it here?"

"I love it here," she admitted, then bit her lip. "I just think I need to go off on my own for a while."

He waited, as if expecting her to clarify her cryptic statement, then shrugged. "Okay. Personal reasons. But I've got to tell you, Martha, this place is great for personal reasons. Look at what happened when my father got sick. No questions asked—Blake sent me home and told me not to worry about a thing. I could focus on my parents, take care of them and not have to worry about my job. You don't always find that kind of caring in a company. You do always find it here."

"I know."

"And *I* need you here," he added. "You've got such a good head for business. Blake can be kind of...well, you know...flaky."

"He's improved," Martha argued. "He makes executive decisions and they're good ones. He runs meetings. He seems to have come to terms with the fact that he's a CEO."

"Yeah," Doug conceded. "But I still need someone like you, an ally to keep Blake on track."

"You'll hire someone like me to replace me," she said.

"Blake might not listen to someone else. He'll listen

to you. I honestly think—" Doug leaned forward, confiding in her "—that he's been acting more like a CEO because he wants to impress you."

"Impress me?" She laughed nervously. "Why would he want to impress me?"

"I don't know. But it's like...maybe you haven't noticed this, but I have. At the meetings, whenever he makes a proposal, he always shoots a look your way to measure your reaction. When he makes a pronouncement, he watches you. I think he's trying to show you what a good manager he can be."

Doug's insinuation unnerved her. Blake had plenty of ways to impress her, and he'd demonstrated most of them the night after the company's holiday party. As far as impressing her at work, though... "He's being a good manager because that's what his company needs."

"I think you bring out the best in him." Doug looked earnest, leaning forward as if he were confiding a vital secret, one that had less to do with work than with Blake himself.

If she'd brought out the best in Blake, he would have fallen in love with her, wouldn't he? He would have adored her and been grateful to her, and dropped to his knees before her, offering her his heart. Maybe he didn't want her bringing out his best, she reminded herself. Maybe he wanted to be just what he was, and nothing better.

It didn't matter what he wanted to be. He hadn't asked Martha to stand by his side as he became that better person. That was why she had to leave.

"This is all very flattering," she said. "You're giving me more credit than I deserve—"

"No. You do deserve it. Without you here, everything's going to fall apart. I was here before you came. Blake's Brews wasn't the place it is now."

"I can't take credit for that."

"You can," Doug insisted, leaning forward and squeezing her hand. "You should. It's true. Ask anyone. Ask Blake."

"Ask me what?"

Martha flinched and craned her neck to peek around Doug. Blake filled the open doorway, tall and lean and so handsome she wanted to weep. His eyes were riveting and his jaw was set. He arched his hand around the doorjamb, his knuckles bloodless with tension.

"I was talking with Martha about—" twisting in his chair, Doug seemed to shrink beneath the fierce power of Blake's stare "—her decision," he concluded weakly.

"That's what I want to talk to her about," Blake announced, stalking into the office. It was relatively spacious, but it seemed much too small with him in it. He seemed to draw all the air out of the room and into himself, all the energy.

Obviously, he knew what decision Doug was referring to. Penny must have informed him. If only Martha could scoot past him and hide in the supply closet, like the spineless wimp she was. She didn't want to discuss her decision with him.

She should have known she'd have to. Even if there had been no personal connection between her and Blake, she would have had to tell him she was resigning. He was her boss, after all.

"Leave," Blake said to Doug. It wasn't like him to order his underlings around, or to be discourteous, but he was steaming, fuming, apparently ready to explode.

She realized she had never seen Blake angry before. She'd never even considered him capable of anger. She noticed a flicker of surprise in Doug's expression, but he dutifully rose, nodded his farewell to Martha and backed out of the office, his puzzled gaze lingering on Blake until Blake closed the door in his face. At least he didn't slam it.

"That was rude," she said, relieved she was able to talk in a normal voice.

Blake didn't bother to argue. He crossed the room to her desk and threw himself into the chair Doug had vacated. He stared at her, his gaze so mesmerizing she couldn't bring herself to look away. She was vaguely aware that he had on jeans and a sweater almost as blue as his eyes, and that his hair was mussed, as if he'd been tearing at it. She inhaled his clean, spicy smell, a fragrance that stirred erotic memories inside her.

He was in her office on business, not pleasure, she acknowledged sadly. He hadn't come to tell her that after thinking things over during the holidays, he'd decided that he was madly in love with her. "Penny told me you're quitting," he growled more than said.

"I've handed in my resignation," she confirmed.

"You can't quit. I won't accept your resignation."

"The hell you won't!" she retorted, finding strength in her own anger. "If you don't like it, fire me!"

"Martha." His voice was rusty, almost broken, and she realized he was fighting his emotions, too. The only problem was that his emotions weren't the emotions she wanted them to be. "I don't want you to go. I'll do whatever you want. I'll pretend—I'll pretend anything. I'll forget anything. Just don't quit. I need you here."

He needed her *here,* at work. He didn't need her in his bed, in his life. Only here, at Blake's Fruit Brews, monitoring the company's finances.

"I can't forget," she admitted, the anger gone from her, replaced by acceptance laced with sorrow. "I shouldn't have become involved with you, Blake. It was a mistake, but we can't undo what we've done. And I can't forget about it. I can't pretend it didn't happen. Neither can you. We both tried that and it didn't work."

"That was because we didn't really want to forget," he pointed out. "We wanted each other. I still want you. But to keep you here, I'm willing..." He stumbled to a halt, apparently unsure what he was willing to do.

"You're willing to what? Stop wanting me? That should be easy for you." She shook her head and said, "It's *me,* Blake. *I* can't stay here. I've got to go."

"Did I hurt you that badly?" He appeared genuinely contrite. "I never wanted to hurt you, Martha."

"It isn't about hurt," she fibbed. Just sitting so close to him hurt her. Seeing him and remembering, wanting more of him than he could give, hurt like a sadist's maliciously conceived torture. "It's about dignity," she explained. "It's about pride. I can't work here anymore."

She prayed she wouldn't have to explain further. Her tears threatened to overflow, and her hands were trembling in her lap. The worst part was that she was desperate to be comforted—by him. She wanted him to put his arms around her and offer his shoulder for her to cry on. She wanted him to kiss the crown of her head and murmur that he understood, that he was sorry, that he would make everything better.

He couldn't make anything better, not without acknowledging that he loved her. And he didn't love her. So there was nothing he could do.

Except let her go.

11

CAPE COD WINTERS were usually dicey. Before he'd started Blake's Fruit Brews, he used to spend his winters picking up temp work tending bar at parties, handling part-time stints at the resorts when something special—like a company holiday party—was happening, and getting paid by the day to do repair work on dry-docked boats. The weather was rarely pretty; nor'easters chewed up the shoreline, snowfall was sporadic and not especially picturesque, and the air was raw and wet.

Blake had the soul of a beachboy, though, and he needed to live near the ocean, no matter what the season. He understood that you had to get through winter to reach summer. Winter was the price you paid for living on the Cape, the cost of breathing in the sun-warmed sea for six months of the year, for having white sand sprinkled in the lawn of your front yard, for being able to drive in a vintage Mustang convertible with the top down and let the wind tangle in your hair. He'd always survived the winters just fine.

Not this year. This year everything was wrong. The sky was too dark during the daytime, and the nights were too long. Two months lay between him and daylight saving time, when the days would start stretching out and the sun would stick around into the evening.

His house seemed cold all the time. No matter how high he set the thermostat, no matter how many split logs he added to the fireplace in his den, he felt a constant chill.

Work failed to thaw him out. The company was going great guns, the bottling plant near Chicago was progressing faster than anyone had anticipated, Good Earth's first orders were strong and Bruno Thompson was confident that the bottled juices would sell like crazy.

Blake couldn't bring himself to care.

He missed Martha.

It was stupid. She was a woman. A very nice woman. An extremely smart woman. An inexplicably sexy woman. But really, just a woman. He'd known women before, and he would get to know women again—ideally, women who weren't poking around in his soul, searching for love, demanding something he wasn't ready to give.

No matter how often he told himself that, he couldn't bring himself to believe it. It was like that dinner date he'd set up after Chicago: he'd been forcing himself, going through the motions and wishing he was with Martha instead of the woman he was with. To take a woman out now would be the same thing. He'd spend the whole time thinking about Martha, being annoyed and angry and lonely and disappointed because the woman he was with couldn't be someone else.

Staff meetings were excruciating. The empty chair where Martha ought to be sitting mocked Blake, nagged him, smacked into his soul like a sucker punch. Penny's memos concerning the applicants she'd interviewed for Martha's old accounting job, and Helen's incessant questions about whether he was going to hire a new financial officer, grated on him. Didn't they realize that Martha was irreplaceable?

He sat in his office, ignoring the stack of papers piled up on his desk that awaited his attention, and thought about how uncharacteristic it was for him to be suffering the blues. He'd never been melancholy. He'd always assumed he'd lacked the gene for that particular mood. Apparently he was wrong. Martha had mutated him.

Staring out his window, he almost didn't see the flurries drifting aimlessly through the air. The sky was gloomy gray, just like his state of mind. "Wake up," Doug shouted at him.

Blake flinched, jerking his gaze from the window to find his trusted lieutenant standing just inches from his desk. When had Doug come in? How long had he been standing there, gaping at Blake without Blake's noticing his presence?

"Sorry," Blake said, attempting a smile. His mouth resisted, curving into a scowl.

"Blake, we've got a problem," Doug announced.

"Do we?" Blake was lethargic, horny, lonely and grouchy. That added up to four problems, as far as he was concerned.

"The new accountant says he's not going to be able to get all our tax records together without help. He wants to hire a temp."

"So? Is that such a big deal?"

Doug looked immensely frustrated. "Of course it's a big deal! We're spending a small fortune to train him, and he wants us to spend even more to bring in extra help. Martha used to be able to do it all by her-

self. Even after she got her promotion, she was still doing accounting work."

"Didn't she leave everything in order?" Blake
couldn't believe she would have deliberately sabo-
taged the records when she'd left. She might hate him,
but she was so damned organized and ethical, he
couldn't imagine her leaving her records in anything
other than pristine condition.

"Of course she left everything in order," Doug
railed. "I went over the records with him. Not like I'm
an accountant or anything, but she had everything set
up for him. He's a nitwit."

"Penny told me he was the best of all the people she
interviewed."

"Sure. January on the Cape, the only people apply-
ing for jobs are chambermaids and waiters."

"Well, we're stuck with him for now," Blake said
with a shrug, reminding himself that he really ought
to share Doug's concern, if only to make Doug feel
better. "Can you continue to work with him?"

"Like I don't have enough to do? I think you're fail-
ing to recognize the gravity of the situation." Doug
flopped into a chair, as if crushed by all the anxiety
pressing down on him. "Why did you let Martha go?"
he wailed quietly. "Why did you accept her resignation?"

Blake couldn't tell Doug the real reason: because
he'd broken her heart. Because he'd crossed all sorts of
lines with her that he shouldn't have, and she'd
crossed lines she would probably never forgive herself for crossing, and she couldn't bear to be near him
anymore. "She wanted to leave, and I wanted her to
be happy," he said, astonished to realize that that was
the truth. He truly did want her happy.

"What about *you* being happy?" Doug's gaze narrowed on Blake. "Your company's booming, we're growing, we've got more responsibilities to face—and you look like you just got news of a loved one's death. What's going on with you, Blake?"

"Nothing." Blake shrugged. "A New Year's hangover."

"New Year's Eve was over a month ago." Doug shook his head. "You were so upbeat last fall, too. When you salvaged the Good Earth deal—"

"Martha salvaged it," Blake muttered, then grimaced at the memory. "We salvaged it together," he added sullenly.

"However it happened, it was good news. Everyone was pumped up about it. We did some hiring. Gave promotions, gave a party, gave bonuses. We were on a roll. And now...it's like you've rolled to a standstill."

"What is this?" Blake attempted a show of indignation. "Psychoanalyze-the-boss time?"

Doug looked even more concerned, peering at Blake through his glasses, hunching forward as if he were going to pat Blake's shoulder in sympathy. "I want to know if something's wrong," he said. "For the sake of the company, and for the sake of our friendship."

"You really want to know?" Blake scrambled for a reasonable lie and came up empty. Lacking a better option, he resorted to honesty. "My love life sucks."

"Really?" Doug apparently hadn't been expecting that answer. He took a moment to digest it, then sighed deeply, a sound that whooshed out of him from the base of his lungs. "After my divorce, my love life was the pits," he confessed. "But now I've got my hands full. You want me to fix you up with someone?"

Blake blinked in surprise. He'd never guessed Doug had more than he could handle in the romance department. Cripes, he'd been trying to set Doug up with Martha! What a waste that would have been—except he was still half-convinced that Doug and Martha were a perfect match. He wondered if Martha had her hands full, too, if she was fending off suitors, passing her excess along to her single girlfriends.

"What do you say?" Doug asked hopefully. "Do you want me to introduce you to someone? We could double date."

"I don't need your help," Blake cut him off. "I'll work it out. Don't worry about me. Just make sure I don't screw the company into the ground while I'm distracted."

"That I can do." Doug stood, then gave in to the urge to give Blake's shoulder a squeeze. It was all Blake could do not to smack his hand away. "Seriously, pal, let me know if you need anything. Someone to come over with a six-pack of beer, someone to remind you that most women aren't worth it. Whoever she was, Blake, whoever did this to you—"

"She was worth it," Blake insisted before Doug could say anything more. He didn't think that was true, but long after Doug had left him in the office, long after he'd resumed the absorbing activity of watching the flurries outside his window, long after he told himself a million times that Martha was history and he should put her out of his mind forever, he couldn't convince himself it wasn't true, either.

MARTHA STARED at the three books on her kitchen table: *She Loves Me—Knot!*, a guide to macramé; *Petal to the Metal*, a book on flower arranging, and *Whatever You Knead*, a bread-baking cookbook. She'd bought them all at the mall, thinking that maybe her sister Nancy was right and she ought to be creative.

"What do you think, Lucy?" she asked, lifting each book in turn, staring at it listlessly and dropping it back onto the table. "How should I waste my time?"

Lucy gave a spirited bark and barreled headfirst into the back door. Pounding her head against a hard surface didn't seem like the sort of hobby Martha wanted to cultivate, even though she felt as if she'd been doing exactly that for the past few months.

"Nancy says I need to break out, try new things, stop restricting myself to the straight and narrow," she told Lucy, touching first one and then another of her new how-to books. "Macramé is basically tying strings in knots." That, too, seemed like an apt a metaphor for her life, or at least her emotions. "Flowers might be more cheerful, especially now." February was such a dreary month. Perhaps if she filled her house with flowers, she'd feel...

Romantic. Bad idea.

"Maybe I'll learn how to bake bread. What do you think, Lucy? Can you picture me as an earth mother type?"

Lucy barked louder and slammed into the door again.

Martha could take a hint. She pulled the leash down from the hook by the door, clipped it onto Lucy's collar, and yanked her fleece cloche down over her ears. So much for her expensive haircut—after a long walk on a chilly Saturday afternoon, she was going to wind up with hat-hair.

As if it mattered what her hair looked like. She had no interest in impressing anyone with her coiffure. One of the best things about Lucy was that she didn't care what Martha looked like. As long as Martha was stroking her or feeding her or taking her to the beach, she received Lucy's undying love.

Lucy adored being outdoors, even if it was thirty raw, blustery degrees out. Ridges of gray snow lined the curbs, waiting for March to melt them away. The trees were barren, the shrubs leafless and patches of visible grass were the color of straw. A perfect day for baking bread or tying string in knots, Martha thought, scowling at having to be outside with her cabin-feverish dog.

Lucy ambled along, sniffing at everything, tugging at her leash as she bounded ahead and then dawdling, forcing Martha to tug the leash from her end. As dreary as the Cape was at this time of year, Martha was grateful that she hadn't been forced to relocate. She'd landed a job with a storefront tax preparation chain. They'd been thrilled to have someone of her ability. Although they hadn't been able to match her previous salary, they hadn't asked her why she'd left Blake's Fruit Brews. She considered the cut in pay offset by the chance to recuperate in private, without having the cause of her pain just down the hall from her or seated across from her at a meeting. As it was, Blake had taken up permanent residence in her mind. She didn't want to have to see him every day, too.

The second most idiotic thing she'd ever done was to tell Blake she loved him. The most idiotic thing was to have fallen in love with him in the first place. "Never fall in love, Lucy," she told her dog, who seemed enthralled by the scent of a holly bush. "If you're stupid enough to fall in love, don't let it be with someone inappropriate—like a gorgeous blond hunk or your boss, or both." Lucy nuzzled her snout under the lower branches. "And if you're stupid enough to fall in love with your gorgeous blond hunk of a boss, don't tell him. Keep a lid on it. Honesty isn't always the best policy."

She missed Blake. If she hadn't opened her mouth, she might have still been working at Blake's Brews, still spending nights in his bed every now and then. She could have continued their affair for as long as he'd been willing. How many more days of happiness could she have known before the truth finally came out? How much more joy?

"But then—" she yanked at the leash and Lucy reluctantly abandoned the holly bush "—when the truth emerged, it would have hurt twice as much. A thousand times as much," she corrected herself.

They reached the beach. It was vacant except for what the sea had washed up—tangles of rust-colored seaweed, shells, shiny pebbles. No footsteps marred the damp, packed sand. The water was the color of slate.

When winter had first arrived, she'd loved the beach. She'd loved the expansive emptiness of it, the frigid winds and the ominous roll of the winter surf. At one time, she'd entertained thoughts of walking along this stretch of sand hand in hand with Blake. She'd imagined him lifting a stick and tossing it for Lucy to fetch, and then hunkering down and scratching Lucy's ribs while she slobbered and swooned in ecstasy. And then the three of them would walk back to Martha's house, where she would fill Lucy's bowls with water and chopped sirloin and then go upstairs to her room with Blake. They would smell the sea as they shed their clothes. He would make love with her like her dream lover, only the dream would be real.

"I'm not cut out for romance, Lucy," she said to her dog, who was in heaven, sniffing every snarl of seaweed, every wet log, the molted shell of a horseshoe crab, the algae clinging to a rock.

She needed a new dream. A nice beach walk with Lucy, and then they'd go home, and Martha would feed Lucy her chopped sirloin and water, and she'd arrange flowers and tie ropes into wall hangings.

She was going to have to do more than develop a new hobby. She was going to have to start her own business. The tax preparation work would carry her until the end of April, by which time she could lay the foundation for opening her own office. She would advertise, hang out a sign, stick her business card into all her neighbors' mailboxes. If she could be the chief financial officer of a fruit juice company, she could certainly run her own business.

Maybe she'd fall in love with that, she thought with forced optimism. Maybe if she fell in love with her work, she wouldn't have any time or energy left to be thinking about the man she'd fallen in love with.

THIS IS THE LAST TIME, Blake promised himself as he cruised slowly down Martha's street. He'd driven past her house two dozen times in the past month, and he was beginning to fear he'd turned into a stalker.

He wasn't stalking Martha, though. He was just driving past her house. Again.

Last time he'd driven this way, he'd had to steer around lingering patches of slush on the pavement. Today, March was offering a preview of spring. The slush had melted into murky puddles, the sky was blue and he'd lowered the convertible top of his car, even though it was really too cold for it.

He didn't understand his compulsion to cruise down her street. More than two months had passed since she'd handed in her resignation, five and a half weeks since she'd actually left. He had no idea where she was working; if she'd informed anyone at Blake's Fruit Brews, he hadn't heard about it. For all he knew, she might have returned to Boston and her previous job. She might have sold her house—except he probably would have noticed a For Sale sign by the curb. He'd certainly checked out the property often enough.

What would he do if he saw her? If she was standing on the front step, or raking away all the crud winter had left in her yard, would he stop and say hello? Ask how she was doing? He wanted to believe he could pull that off, nice and smooth. But he wasn't sure. The sight of her might make him do something stupid, like say, "How about a quick roll in the hay, for old times' sake?"

He might even get soppy and say, "I've really missed you." Which was true, but which she might interpret to mean he loved her. What he missed about her was her intelligence, the way she inspired him to work harder, to conceptualize and plan and lead his company. He missed conversations with her. He missed her laughter. He missed her kisses, her scent, the way she clung to him when she climaxed.

None of that had anything to do with love. But if he said anything the least bit sentimental, she might think it did. Women were prone to such misunderstandings.

Fortunately, she wasn't outside, so what he would

say to her was no longer an issue. He slowed to a stop, inhaling the first faint hints of spring in the air, that thawing-earth scent, the lush, sour fragrance of the ocean wafting inland from the beach a few blocks away. Her house looked good, the yard tidy, no roof shingles missing. He sat in his car, feeling the fresh air wrap around him, and stared at the cozy little house, wondering what the hell he was looking for.

He heard the muffled sound of barking coming from her house. Her dog. Lucy, that was the mutt's name, wasn't it?

Lucy was barking, all right. Barking her fool head off. She must be one of those dogs who went berserk whenever a stranger approached the property.

She hadn't gone crazy the time Blake had approached the property, though, last October, when he'd helped Martha bring her bicycle around to the back porch. Lucy had sounded off with some friendly yapping, but nothing like the frantic howls and growls he was hearing from the house now.

He turned off his engine and listened. It didn't sound like the barks of a watchdog trying to scare off an intruder. It sounded like...desperation. Like Lucy was panicked.

Blake already knew he was a bit unbalanced; he wouldn't have been prowling past Martha's house several times a week for the past month if he was sane. But he was positive Martha's dog was trying to communicate something. Something bad.

He climbed out of his car and walked up the unpaved driveway. The closer he got to the house, the wilder the dog sounded. He assured himself that the worst that would happen would be if Martha was home and she and the dog were fine. He'd have to explain what he was doing driving past her house—he'd think of some likely story—and why he thought her dog sounded ominous. Or he'd say he was in the neighborhood and just dropped by to see how she was doing...and, oh, since he was here, how about a quick roll in the hay, for old times' sake?

He reached the steps to the screened back porch, and the dog sounded hysterical. Picking up his pace, he climbed the steps and crossed the porch. Her deck furniture looked okay, but her bicycle was missing. Probably she was riding somewhere.

Did she bike to her new job? Did her new boss give her a lift home if it was too dark for her to bike home at the end of the day? Did she like her new boss as much as she'd liked Blake? Had she gone and fallen in love with someone else? He would be happy for her if she did, he swore. He'd be so damned thrilled for her...

He smelled something—not the ocean, not the first green aromas of spring, but something acrid. He heard a thumping sound, and a scratching. The dog was at the back door, trying to get out.

"Martha?" Blake knocked on the door. The smell was strong—smoke. Oh, God. He pounded on the door with his fist. "Martha!"

The dog barked, a frenzy of howls and scratching.

"Damn it! Martha!" He wrenched the doorknob. Locked. He pounded again, shouted, "Martha!" and coughed from the stench of the smoke.

What if she was hurt in there? Her house burning, and her noble dog trying to summon help—Blake had to get inside. He made one more futile attempt to twist the doorknob, then rammed his shoulder against the door. Again and again, until his arm ached, he threw his full weight against it—and on the fifth shove, the doorjamb splintered and the door swung open.

The dog nearly knocked him over bolting out onto the porch. Not that Blake blamed her. The kitchen reeked and the air was thick with gray smoke. Cursing, Blake held his arm across his face to block the smoke and bellowed Martha's name.

He heard no response.

The smoke wasn't so dense that he couldn't see where it was coming from: the oven. He raced across the room, twisted the switch off and opened the door, releasing a heavy stream of black smoke into the room. He cursed again, then grabbed a pair of oven mitts from the counter next to the range, donned them and reached into the oven. He pulled out a pan holding a large solid brick of something, charred black. Not until he had it in the sink with the cold water spraying down on it did he notice the lump's resemblance to a loaf of bread.

An extremely burned loaf of bread.

He turned off the water, threw open the windows and waved the smoke away. The room still stank, and he ventured into the living room to open a window there. "Martha?" he called again, hoping the smoke hadn't been bad enough to knock her unconscious. She could be lying on the floor somewhere, felled by the fumes.

He surveyed the living room. It had a familiar look about it. He'd been in rooms like it—the comfortable overstuffed sofa, the big easy chair and footrest, the seascape paintings and braided rugs. The carved newel post at the bottom of the stairs looked familiar, too, like the stairways of countless other Cape Cod style houses.

He walked up the stairs, relieved that the smoke hadn't filled the second floor. "Martha?" he called again, even though by now he was pretty sure she wasn't home.

The stairs deposited him in a small hallway with three doors opening off it—two bedrooms and a bathroom. He wasn't sure how he knew what lay behind those three doors, or how he knew which door led to Martha's bedroom. He just knew.

"Martha?" He tapped on her bedroom door, then edged it open, slowly, hesitantly, not quite sure what he expected to find on the other side. When at last he stepped inside, he was overwhelmed by the profound sense that he had been in this room before.

He wasn't into mystical stuff, déja vù, past lives and all that. But as he moved farther into the room, his gaze taking in the brass double bed jutting out from the opposite wall, the blond oak dresser, the freestanding oak-framed mirror, the rocking chair, the pale-blue curtains on the dormer windows and the side window...the night table with its lamp and its clock radio, the digits marking the time in a glowing red beside the plump pillows, the quilted blue spread... He knew how that spread would feel before he touched it.

And he knew how Martha would look in bed. In white cotton pajamas, her eyes dark and expectant, her throat exposed for a kiss, her chest rising and falling with each excited breath...

He fell back a step, stunned by the certainty that he'd been in this room before, with Martha. In bed with her. Making love with her. It had never happened, of course it hadn't, but the sensation was so strong—

A scream from downstairs jolted him from his trance. He spun around, bolted from the room and raced down the stairs.

"Omigod! Omigod!" Martha screamed from the kitchen. He charged into the room, then grabbed the doorjamb to slow himself down. She was standing in the center of the room, a large carving knife in her hand and Lucy scampering in circles around her feet.

"Don't kill me!" Blake yelled.

She blinked, gasped and lowered her hand. He was disheartened by how long it took her to toss the knife onto the counter, as if she had to resist the temptation to plunge the blade into his chest.

"What the hell are you doing here?" she asked. "Breaking into my house—"

"Your house was on fire," he retorted, then shrugged. "Well, a loaf of bread in your oven was on fire, anyway." He pointed toward the sink.

She glanced into the basin and winced. Turning from Blake, she moved to the sink and lifted the charred remains of the bread. Wrinkling her nose, she dropped it, pan and all, into the trash can.

Now that she was no longer armed, he dared to enter the room. She had jeans and a cream-colored sweatshirt on, and her hair was windblown. Her butt filled the jeans really nicely, he noted.

When she turned back to him, he had a chance to admire her face, too. It was still full of angles and hollows, not the sort of face that would have fashion magazines begging her to appear on their covers but a beautiful face nonetheless, a face that could haunt him forever if he let it.

"How did you get in here?" she asked, bristling with suspicion.

He motioned toward the back door with its splintered lock. "I think it's obvious how I got in."

"Why?"

"I was—" *driving past your house because I'm slightly deranged and can't seem to help myself* "—in the neighborhood and I heard your dog barking her head off. I thought something might be wrong. As it turned out, something *was* wrong."

"What? A loaf of bread burned in the oven?"

"The whole kitchen was full of smoke," he defended himself. "Your dog was going crazy. I had no idea where the smoke was coming from until I broke in. I hollered first, knocked on the door—and when you didn't respond I thought you might have been hurt." He put on his best indignant look. "Some people would call me a hero."

"And some would call you an intruder." But the tension seemed to melt from her shoulders, and she slid the knife back into a drawer and shoved it shut with her hip. "I wasn't going to stab you, Blake," she said quietly. "I came home from a bike ride and it looked as if someone had broken into my house. Well, someone did," she added, frowning at the damage to her back door. "You can't blame me for being alarmed."

He could blame her for being stubborn and unrealistic, for quitting her job at Blake's Brews and insisting that a rip-roaring relationship had to be love or she would want no part of it, but he couldn't blame her for assuming a burglar was lurking inside her house. Standing so close to her, he realized he'd been scared out of his wits that something bad might have happened to her. He hadn't stopped to consider what she would think if he broke down her door. He'd been too worried that she was inside, in trouble.

He studied her now, just a few feet away from him, and realized that maybe he was the one in trouble. Even knowing that she'd once loved him, and that he'd disappointed her, and that she was determined not to let him hurt her, he wanted her.

"How have you been?" he asked.

She lifted her gaze as high as his chin, but couldn't seem to bring herself to look into his eyes. "I'm fine," she said quietly. "How are you?"

He shrugged. "The new accountant isn't as good as you were, but we're getting by." He wanted to kiss her. "Did you find another job?"

She nodded. "It's all right. I can't complain."

He heard a complaint in her tone, though. *We're both miserable*, he almost said. *Why won't you come back? Why did you have to ruin everything by dragging love into it? Why don't we forget all about love and go upstairs to your room, so I can figure out why I felt so positive I'd been in it before? And then we could make love, so I can replace that weird déja vù feeling with the real thing.*

"I'd better go." That was definitely *not* what he wanted to say, but he didn't dare to say what he was thinking. Before he'd known Martha, he wouldn't have been so chicken. Before he'd known Martha, none of it would have mattered.

Everything mattered now, in ways he couldn't fathom. Everything, from the pulse-pounding fear that had driven him to break down her door to the eerie sensation he'd had in her bedroom, to this moment in her kitchen, when every impulse in him clamored for him to haul her into his arms and kiss her until she wanted what he wanted—it all mattered.

And there was nothing he could do about it. Nothing but walk away.

LONG AFTER Blake was gone, her heart was still pounding.

She should have thanked him for breaking down her door and turning off her oven before the bread burst into flames or smoke engulfed the whole house. He might have saved Lucy's life. Yes, he was a hero, and she should have told him so.

In any case, she was ready to abandon her efforts at making bread. She'd given up on macramé after her third attempt: the belt she'd knotted looked ugly, the plant hanger was lopsided, and the wall hanging resembled a moth-eaten burlap sack. It was too early in the spring for flowers, so she'd decided to skip flower arranging and try her hand at baking.

She'd nearly set her house on fire.

She was a disaster. Even worse, she was rude. She should have thanked Blake, thrown herself at his feet and confessed that she missed him every day, every night, every waking minute and every sleeping one, too. She should have told him she was willing to be with him on his terms, abandoning all thoughts of love and forever-after. She could have deferred her heartache if she had to, lived for today and saved her tears for the inevitable tomorrow when he grew tired of the relationship and moved on.

She was no better at accepting the crumbs of an unrequited passion than she was at baking bread or tying string into artistic knots, though. The only thing she was good at, she acknowledged, was working with numbers, playing by the rules, being a quiet, mousy accountant.

"How are you doing, Lucy?" she asked her dog, who had plunged her snout into her water dish. Clearly, the afternoon's turmoil had driven her to drink.

Lucy glanced up. Martha tried to convince herself that dogs could not look reproving, but Lucy certainly looked peeved. "You liked him, I know," Martha said, deciding she needed a drink, too. She pulled a bottle of spring water from the refrigerator and twisted off the cap. "But you like anyone who scratches your ribs. You're too promiscuous."

Lucy seemed to curl her lip before dunking back into the water for another guzzle.

Martha trudged up the stairs, gripping her bottle and reviewing the events of the past few minutes, from her horrified discovery that her lock had been broken to Blake's departure. What had he been doing in her neighborhood? She'd vaguely noticed a convertible car that looked like his Mustang parked outside her house, but she'd been so distracted by Lucy's loud barking—from the porch, when Martha had known she'd left Lucy locked up inside the house— that she hadn't dwelled on the significance of the car.

Inside her bedroom, she crossed to the dresser and reached for her brush to untangle her hair. Peering into the mirror, she frowned. Something was different. Not her, but the room reflected in the glass.

She pivoted and scrutinized her bedroom slowly, meticulously. Nothing seemed out of place. Her bed was neatly made, her drapes open to let in the afternoon sun, her bathrobe draped across the rocker where she'd left it that morning. Yet the room looked different. It *felt* different.

"I want my room back," she murmured, pretending

she was talking to Lucy so she wouldn't feel like a complete lunatic. "I want my life back."

But she'd lost that comfort and safety last October, when this room had been invaded by a fantasy. The possibility that her entire universe had been permanently altered that night, that the gift she'd accepted had changed everything for all time, was infinitely more frightening than coming home to find her back door broken and her kitchen filled with smoke. In fact, it was the most frightening idea in the world.

12

MARCH BLEW OUT like a lamb. Early tulips began to poke their spiky green leaves through the thawed earth, the scent of the ocean began to sweep pleasantly inland, and Blake discovered that he was still functioning.

He hadn't driven past Martha's house since the day he'd broken in. He hadn't forgiven himself for not dragging her into his arms and kissing her into submission when he'd had the chance, but he was, if not cured, gradually recovering from his obsession with her. She wasn't his type and he wasn't hers, and never the twain would meet, or however that old saying went. He was coming to his senses. He was going to be all right, eventually.

He stayed focused on his work, bringing documents home on the weekends to study so he wouldn't fritter away his Saturdays trying to come up with reasons not to drive through her neighborhood. He was on an anti-Martha crusade, and he was willing to do anything to shut her out of his mind—even work on the weekends.

He received an invitation to Tracy Thompson's wedding. "I think you should go," Doug advised him. "The Good Earth chain is doing great things for us in the Midwest. I think it would be a shrewd move to strengthen your friendship with Bruno."

"I had an affair with the bride," Blake reminded Doug, staring at the elegantly embossed invitation and shaking his head. "How can I go to her wedding?"

"Just go. Be nice. Shake the groom's hand and don't mention that you spent some hot nights in Jamaica with Tracy." Blake must have looked extremely dubious, because Doug added, "The last time you went to Chicago, you came back a changed man, full of energy and ideas. That city is a tonic for you. I think you should go."

The last time Blake had come back from Chicago, he'd come back as Martha's lover. That was what had energized him. The city had nothing to do with it.

He sent a note to Tracy expressing his regrets, and sent the happy couple a set of silver-trimmed crystal soda fountain glasses and a case of Blake's Fruit Brews.

He was going to be fine, he promised himself. He was like a recovering alcoholic, taking it one day at a time, commending himself whenever he thought about Martha without suffering pangs of loneliness or horniness or undefined regret. Eventually, he hoped, he would no longer think about her at all.

Nights were more difficult than days, but at least he was alone at night, so no one could see him at his worst. He would lie in bed and remember the weight of her body draped across his, her hair tickling his chin, her hand roaming aimlessly across his chest and shoulder and then developing a keen sense of direction and journeying straight down his body, zeroing in on its target. Remembering would make him hard, and then sleep would be all but impossible. He wondered if maybe bringing another woman to his bed would help, but he was afraid if he tried to make love with another woman, he would do something unconscionable, like close his eyes and wish she were Martha.

He wondered where she was working, how she was faring, whether she had installed an effective smoke detector in her kitchen. He wondered why she'd been baking bread that day. Martha was hardly a gourmet chef. She liked to ride her bicycle, and Hyannis had a few good bakeries within biking distance of her house. Maybe he ought to drive by, just to make sure the place hadn't gone up in smoke.

No. Like the recovering alcoholic who couldn't trust himself to walk past a tavern, Blake couldn't trust himself to drive past her house. Not yet. Maybe in a while, when he was more fully in control of himself.

The first Saturday night in April found him home alone, as usual. He dragged the gas grill out onto the deck from the garage, flame-broiled a hamburger, and consumed it, along with a bottle of beer, in front of the television. In normal times, he would have been on a date, dining at one of the seaside restaurants or maybe sharing enchiladas and quesadillas at his favorite Mexican restaurant near the airport, and then heading off to a movie at the Cineplex. But things hadn't been normal since he'd turned his clock back an hour last October.

Tonight he would be turning it ahead again. Daylight saving time was scheduled to begin when 2:00 a.m. jumped to 3:00 a.m. He'd always loved the fall part of daylight saving, when he got that bonus hour. In April, however, that hour was snatched back. He didn't like it, but whoever was running the planet hadn't given him a vote.

If his life was normal, he wouldn't mind parting with a precious hour; he'd be so busy doing fun things with his date that he wouldn't have even noticed the loss. But thanks to Martha, he noticed everything these days, every disappointment, every sacrifice.

He watched TV until boredom unlatched the door and allowed a few thoughts of Martha to sneak in—how much fun it had been watching a bad movie with her, how much he'd enjoyed talking to her, how strangely familiar her bedroom had seemed to him that day he'd gone inside her house. Appalled, he shoved those thoughts back out of his mind and locked it tight against another invasion. Turning off the tube, he trudged down the hall to the bathroom, peeled off his clothes and took a long shower. After toweling off, he ran a comb through his hair and headed to his bedroom, to bed.

He was weary, he realized. Exhausted, as if he'd run a marathon. Drained, the way he felt after making love with Martha—only after making love with her, he was always smiling, satisfied, downright pleased to find himself too fatigued to move. Right now, he was fatigued, but pleasure had nothing to do with it.

He reached for the switch and clicked off the lamp beside his bed. His alarm clock read twelve forty-five. He ought to turn the clock ahead an hour, but he was too tired. He'd switch that clock, and all the rest of the clocks in his house, tomorrow.

Sleep dropped a dark blanket over him, but it wasn't warm or comforting. He heard a ticking, even though his bedside clock was electric and didn't tick. It was probably just a tree branch tapping on the roof, or the radiators rattling as hot water streamed through them, or the beating of his pulse.

He was abruptly aware that someone had entered his room. Maybe he hadn't heard it, maybe he'd only sensed it, because all he could hear was the ticking. He sat up and saw her—a shadow of a woman, a silhouette, a ghost.

No, not a ghost. It was Martha, and Martha was alive, so she couldn't be a ghost. She was merely...a *presence.* He smelled Martha's clean, fresh scent and felt her warmth permeating the room. A smile spread across his face. Martha was here, in his bedroom, approaching his bed. He didn't care if this was a dream. It was the best dream he'd had in ages.

He extended his arms toward her, and she fell back. "No," she whispered. He couldn't hear her voice, but in that one word, that one breath, he was positive he could identify her.

"Come here," he said, still smiling. It wasn't like her to play flirty and hard to get, but if that was her game he'd go along with it, as long as it ended with her in his bed, in his arms.

"This is no gift," she whispered, her voice as insubstantial as her body. He could barely see her, the room was so dark.

"I'll give you a gift," he promised. "Just come here and I'll give you whatever you want."

"You've lost an hour. It's gone. It's lost."

Skirting his bed, she glided to his alarm clock. She was so close to him, he should have been able to grab her, yet he was unable to move his arms, unable to shift his body to that side of the bed. All he could see was the shadow of her blocking his view of his clock. "There," she whispered. "It's done now. That hour is lost."

She drew back and he saw the luminous face of his

clock reading three o'clock. Inexplicably angry, he turned to yell at her for tampering with his clock—and she was gone.

He howled, then opened his eyes to find himself sitting in the middle of his bed, naked and drenched in sweat, his heart pounding fiercely and his lungs pumping. "Just a dream," he murmured, trying to calm himself down. "Just a bad dream."

He couldn't remember the last time he'd had a nightmare. Probably not since he was a kid, suffering those stereotypical dreams about showing up at school stark naked and unprepared on the day of the final exam. But he was a happy, healthy guy with no skeletons in his closets and no unresolved psychological problems in his subconscious. Nightmares were for neurotics, not for him.

This had seemed too real to be a nightmare, anyway. As his eyes adjusted to the dark, he noticed that his bedroom door was closed. However real it had seemed, he knew it had been a dream. Martha could not have passed through a closed door, and he hadn't heard anyone open or shut it.

Still, he felt shaken and uneasy. He twisted to turn on the lamp—and jumped. His clock read three o'clock.

"Big deal," he told himself, although his heart was thumping crazily again. He'd probably been asleep for an hour, he'd had this dream, and he'd awakened to discover that his clock had marked off the hour.

Just to be sure, he swung out of bed and crossed the room to his dresser, where he'd left his watch. Squinting, he read the dial: two o'clock.

His heart went from galloping speed to a dead standstill. He angled the watch so he could see the second hand as it made its even sweep around the dial, proof that the watch hadn't stopped running.

"All right," he muttered, desperate to assure himself he wasn't totally insane. He must have bumped one of the buttons on the clock, that was all. When he'd stretched to turn off the lamp, he must have hit the Hour Set button with his elbow—except that the buttons were tucked into the back of the clock to prevent a person from hitting one accidentally.

Someone had deliberately reset his clock. Not Blake, because he would have reset his watch if he'd reset his clock. Someone else. The phantom had done it, that woman he'd dreamed, the one who kept whispering that it was lost.

"You've lost your mind, that's what," Blake told himself.

But her whispered refrain echoed inside him: *It's gone. It's lost.*

She hadn't been talking about his mind. She'd been talking about the hour he'd lost—and something else, a much greater loss. The loss of the most precious gift he'd ever had.

Martha's love.

MARTHA HADN'T BEEN asleep more than an hour when Lucy began yapping. She'd intended to get to bed earlier, but she'd felt obliged to read her book on flower arranging from cover to cover in search of a single arrangement she felt capable of copying. She had a premonition that she was going to be as ill-suited for flower arranging as she'd been for bread baking and macramé. Bonsai trees were gorgeous, but she doubted she'd be able to train them. She could scarcely train her dog, after all. She couldn't even train herself not to let love turn her into a fool. How was she going to get a miniature tree to obey her?

She'd tossed the book aside and wandered through her house, resetting all the clocks an hour ahead before she went to sleep. It had taken her longer than she'd expected to reformat the clock in her VCR—the buttons had been stubborn, the battery in the remote control losing power. By the time she'd finished with it, midnight had come and gone.

She'd had trouble falling asleep. Her body had nagged her that it was an hour earlier than she thought it was. The glowing red digits on her alarm clock had mocked her. But after a long while, she'd managed to drift off.

And now this. Lucy, the untrainable mutt, was singing a canine aria in the dead of night.

Martha cursed, then apologized to Lucy, who was prancing spiritedly back and forth across her bedroom. "Hush," she groaned. "What's the matter with you? Is the house on fire? Did I leave the oven on again?"

Lucy scampered to the bedroom door, nudged it open with her nose and barked some more.

"All right, all right. You win." Disgusted, Martha sat up, lifted her robe from the rocking chair and shoved her arms through the sleeves. Tying the sash, she heard what sounded like a knock on the door. Lucy must have heard it, too, because she gave Martha a sharp bark, as if to say, "I told you so!" and raced through the door to the stairs.

Who on earth would be knocking on her door at this hour? Maybe a neighbor. Maybe someone was sick, or hurt—although certainly her neighbors could telephone her instead of pounding on her door. Maybe a driver had had an accident—in which case, she would keep the door locked and telephone the police.

As she plodded down the stairs, raking her fingers through her mussed hair, she heard the knocking more clearly. It was loud and determined. She sighed, blinked and flicked on the porch light. Making sure the safety chain was fastened, she inched the door open.

Blake stood on the front step, his fist raised as if about to pound the door again. His hair was disheveled, his shirt untucked so the tails hung below the edge of his denim jacket. In the darkness, his eyes seemed illuminated from within, so blue it hurt her to look directly into them.

"What are you doing?" she asked, keeping the chain in place and tightening the lapels of her robe beneath her chin. "Why are you pounding on my door like a maniac?"

"Your doorbell isn't working," he explained.

"I meant..." Cool air seeped through the narrow opening, but she felt warm. She always felt warm when Blake was around. "What are you doing here? Do you know what time it is?"

"I couldn't sleep," he said simply. His smile was half sheepish, half hopeful. "I had a bad dream. In the dream I..." He gazed at her with a longing that ignited an answering longing inside her, as if his eyes had reached all the way to her soul and set it on fire. "I was supposed to lose an hour, but I lost you instead."

She wasn't sure what to say, so she opted for silence. Blake had lost her, but he'd never really wanted her, so it shouldn't count as a true loss. And she couldn't exactly say she was flattered to be considered the equivalent of daylight saving time in his dream.

"Let me in, Martha," he murmured.

She studied him through the crack above the chain. The amber porch light spilled down on him, turning his hair golden and etching the angles of his face in light. She hated him for being so handsome, for being able to arouse her simply by existing. She hated him for showing up at her front door on a night she'd had trouble sleeping—as if she hadn't had trouble sleeping every single night since she'd told him she loved him.

"I love you," he said. "Let me in."

Her heart slammed against her ribs, a bruising pain. Surely he couldn't mean that. He'd say anything to get inside, and once he was inside she would have no defense against him. She would fall in love with him all over again, a thousand times more deeply than she already did. It would be too late.

It was already too late. It was later than it should be, time playing tricks on her and Blake. And the safety lock was no defense against him, anyway. He was already in her heart, and it didn't seem likely that he would ever leave.

Reluctantly, but with a sense of inevitability, she unhooked the chain and opened the door.

He entered the house, closed the door behind him, and studied her in the dim hall light. Lucy sniffed his sneakers and then sat on his feet, as if to tell Martha she was prepared to keep him from walking away.

He hunkered down and scratched Lucy behind the ears. The dog grunted happily.

"Martha," he said, peering up at her. "I've been going crazy for months. I didn't know why until tonight, when you came to me."

"What?" Her fingers fisted around the robe's lapels. "I didn't come to you. You *are* crazy."

"You came into my bedroom while I was asleep."

She laughed nervously. "Don't be silly. You're the one who breaks into people's houses, not me."

He'd broken into her house just the other day, when she'd incinerated that loaf of bread. And he'd broken in last October, the night daylight saving time had ended. He'd come into her bedroom while she was asleep, drifting in on a dream and awakening her to what it would mean to love him.

"Maybe you dreamed I was in your house," she told him, shivering at the thought that he could have had the same dream about her she'd had about him.

"Maybe I did—but it felt so real."

She gazed down at him, at the lush tangle of his hair, his broad shoulders, his hand moving lazily against Lucy's thick fur. "Was the dream—" she cleared her throat "—erotic?"

He chuckled and shook his head. "No, it was awful. You came in and messed with my clock, and told me I'd lost an hour. Only I knew you were telling me I'd lost something much more important. You were right. I *did* lose something more important." He abandoned Lucy and lifted his hands to capture hers. "I lost you. I love you, Martha. It took me this long to realize why I've been going crazy. It's because I lost you, and I love you and I need you in my life."

She had ached to hear him say those words the last time they'd made love. Now, though...could she believe him?

How could she *not* believe him? He was on his knees before her, his hands gripping hers as if she were a lifeline. And his eyes, those hypnotically beautiful eyes that had transfixed her from the first moment she'd seen them, were honest. They'd been honest from the start, and they were honest now. In their dazzling depths she saw love and need.

"Do you still love me?" he asked.

She could only match his honesty. "Yes."

"Can I make the past few months up to you? Can I reset our clocks so everything is right between us?"

She tried to pull him to his feet, but he was too big and strong to move, so she wound up sinking to her knees instead, where they could look at each other as equals. "I'm thinking you'd better do that," she said quietly, tenderly, feeling her love break free, now that she no longer had to suppress it. "Because I'm a failure at baking bread."

"Are those your only two choices?" he asked, obviously bemused. "Either you love me or you bake bread?"

"Or arrange flowers, or play with string. My sister told me to find some activity to keep busy until I got over you. None of them worked. I can't do anything but organize numbers."

"And ride a bike, and take are of Lucy. And think and laugh and make love. And put up with me," he ended hopefully, his voice rising in a question.

"That's about it," she agreed. "I'm pretty much a failure at everything else."

"As long as you can make love and put up with me, the rest doesn't matter." He pulled her to himself and kissed her. Lucy growled in protest when he nudged her with his knee, but he ignored her. "Let's go to bed," he murmured. "I just want to hold you, all night long."

"You don't want to make love with me?" she asked, feigning hurt.

"That, too. As long as it's all night long. As long as it never ends."

"Actually, this might be the shortest night of the year. We did lose that hour, don't forget."

"We found everything we need." He pushed himself to stand, bringing her with him, and then swung her into his arms. "Promise you'll stay with me forever," he said as he started up the stairs.

She hooked her arms around his neck and nuzzled his shoulder. "I'm a stuffy, proper accountant," she reminded him. "If you want forever, you'll have to make it legal."

"Okay. Marry me."

She was afraid to smile. "Do you mean it?"

"Of course I mean it. Marry me, Martha. I know you love me. And I love you. So let's make it legal." He hesitated outside her bedroom door, as if unwilling to take another step until she gave him her answer.

"Are you sure?"

"Positive."

She smiled. "Then yes. I'll marry you."

He nudged the door wider. "It took you long enough to make up your mind," he muttered, feigning annoyance. "It's about time you said yes."

"You're right," she said, smiling up at him as he carried her across the threshold. "It's about time."

MILLS & BOON®

Makes any time special™

Mills & Boon publish 29 new titles every month. Select from...

Modern Romance™   **Tender Romance**™

Sensual Romance™

Medical Romance™   **Historical Romance**™

MAT2

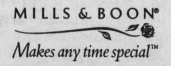

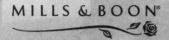

She wished he would kiss her…

Rising on tiptoe, Martha touched her lips to his. Just a light brush of a kiss, nothing aggressive. Nothing that would result in corporate hysteria—the boss and the accountant in a torrid embrace! Just a little peck of friendship and gratitude and—

Blake hauled her into his arms, and notions like friendship and gratitude evaporated. He kissed her the way her dream man had kissed her, only it seemed more real, more true. His arms were so strong, his kiss so greedy, his body so hard and hungry.

Somehow they wound up in his room, the door closed behind them. She had a moment to glimpse his face before he lowered his mouth to hers. *Blake*, she thought, half dazed. He wanted *her*.

He broke the kiss again, his gaze remaining on her face as he removed her jacket. His eyes locked with hers, he didn't need to glance down to find the buttons of her blouse.

Her heart began to beat faster, and her legs began to feel weaker. She was being stripped naked by a man who'd been the lover of her dreams for months…but now he was very, very real…

Her Secret Lover was inspired by a conversation I had with my editor, Malle Vallik, at a conference in Boston on a Saturday evening in April. It was the night when the clocks went forward, and we were reminded by the hotel to set our watches ahead an hour. Malle and I started talking about where that hour went, what happened to it…and I said, 'Imagine if a mystery man would arrive and make passionate love to you on that one magic hour, and then he'd disappear.' Malle and I looked at each other and almost simultaneously said, 'Now, *there's* a great idea for a Temptation®!' I hope you enjoy it as much as I liked writing it!

—Judith Arnold

2 FREE

books and a surprise gift!

We would like to take this opportunity to thank you for reading this Mills & Boon® book by offering you the chance to take TWO more specially selected titles from the Sensual Romance™ series absolutely FREE! We're also making this offer to introduce you to the benefits of the Reader Service™—

★ FREE home delivery
★ FREE gifts and competitions
★ FREE monthly Newsletter
★ Exclusive Reader Service discounts
★ Books available before they're in the shops

Accepting these FREE books and gift places you under no obligation to buy, you may cancel at any time, even after receiving your free shipment. Simply complete your details below and return the entire page to the address below. *You don't even need a stamp!*

YES! Please send me 2 free Sensual Romance books and a surprise gift. I understand that unless you hear from me, I will receive 4 superb new titles every month for just £2.40 each, postage and packing free. I am under no obligation to purchase any books and may cancel my subscription at any time. The free books and gift will be mine to keep in any case.

T0ZEA

Ms/Mrs/Miss/Mr ....Initials......................................
BLOCK CAPITALS PLEASE

Surname ....

Address ....

....

....Postcode....................................

Send this whole page to:
UK: FREEPOST CN81, Croydon, CR9 3WZ
EIRE: PO Box 4546, Kilcock, County Kildare (stamp required)

Offer valid in UK and Eire only and not available to current Reader Service subscribers to this series. We reserve the right to refuse an application and applicants must be aged 18 years or over. Only one application per household. Terms and prices subject to change without notice. Offer expires 31st January 2001. As a result of this application, you may receive further offers from Harlequin Mills & Boon and other carefully selected companies. If you would prefer not to share in this opportunity please write to The Data Manager at the address above.

Mills & Boon® is a registered trademark owned by Harlequin Mills & Boon Limited.
Sensual Romance™ is a registered trademark, used under licence.